ENDGAME

A JACK SIGLER & CHESS TEAM UNIVERSE GUIDEBOOK

JEREMY ROBINSON

WITH KANE GILMOUR

BREAKNECK MEDIA

To all the Jack Sigler / Chess Team fans,
past and future.

TABLE OF CONTENTS

TABLE OF CONTENTS

INTRODUCTION

What you hold in your hands—or what you see on your e-reading device's screen—is a guidebook to the Jack Sigler / Chess Team universe. It's full of information about the characters and events in the previous sixteen novels and novellas that comprise one of Jeremy Robinson's most popular and long-lived series. If you need to catch up, or you just don't remember some of the older books well enough, this guide is for you. But let's face it, we didn't want to just give you summarized chunks of old material. There's a Deep Blue short story here that ties into the new Jack Sigler thriller, *Cannibal*, twenty beautiful pieces of original Christian Guldager artwork and 'eye witness sketches' from Jeremy and the fans themselves. There're also a handful of hints about the future scattered throughout this guide.

I found the first Chess Team book—*Pulse*—in hardcover, at a now defunct chain bookstore in New Hampshire, when it came out in 2009. It was before I had met Jeremy. The cover with the Hydra, and the description about regenerating soldiers won me over, and then the high octane action in the book, combined with smart science and fascinating historical connections had me eager for the next book about this team of special ops soldiers that fought creatures and megalomaniacs. I struck up a correspondence with Jeremy via e-mail, telling him how much I loved the book (and how much I wanted him to put everything out in hardcover—I'm still badgering him for an omnibus hardcover of the Chess Team novellas). We found we had a lot in common, and soon we were friends and e-mailing each other a ridiculous number of times a day, on topics ranging from the music we listen to, to the New England weather and the latest Korean creature films.

I became the editor for his Breakneck Media titles, and one of my earliest tasks was helping him with continuity and editing on the first five Chesspocalypse novellas, shorter stories set in the Chess Team universe and focusing on individual characters from the novels. These novellas would be co-authored with five other great thriller writers. The stories were meant to fill what Jeremy knew would be a long gap between *Threshold* and the fourth book in the series (which ultimately became *Ragnarok*). At the time, it had been two years since Jeremy had written *Threshold*, and the cannon of the series up to that point (*Pulse*, *Instinct*, and *Threshold*) was fresher in my head as a reader and die-hard fan than it was in his as creator. Collaboratively, the Chesspocalypse was a great mix of talent: Jeremy's vision and concepts, the infusion of new ideas from other great writers who were fans of the series and my editorial talent for pedantically championing continuity.

Sean Ellis, a fantastic writer who comes to any brainstorming session armed with reams of notes and a well formed outline, had more ideas than he could fit in *Callsign: King*, and he lobbied to turn it into a trilogy of novellas, so the Chesspocalypse grew. While I was editing these glorious slices of Chess Team goodness, I proposed to Jeremy that he do a Deep Blue story as well, and maybe do it solo. He was well entrenched in writing his next thriller for St. Martin's Press at the time, and he asked if I was interested in helping to write it instead. My own first novel was looking for an agent at the time, and Jeremy had read, enjoyed and even blurbed it for me. He knew he could count on me to throw everything I had into a Chess Team story. So the Chesspocalypse grew again.

As Jeremy's entire body of work grew, he found himself with too many series to write and not enough time, so he engaged Sean and I to help with continuing the Chess Team world once again. *Ragnarok*, *Omega*, *Savage* and the recently released *Cannibal* were the result. Due to events in *Omega*, a new series following Jack Sigler's adventures in time was born, and J. Kent Holloway came aboard to help with that series, dubbed the 'Jack Sigler Continuum.' And now there's another new spin-off series coming in 2015, called the 'Cerberus Group,' following the adventures of George Pierce. (The first book will be called *Herculean*, which ought to tell long-time fans something.) Oh yes, and there'll be a Chess Team short story in a military horror anthology later this year.

That adds up to a lot of continuity, and as you might imagine, as the Keeper of Chess Team Lore, I'm needing to look things up a lot, and I'm fielding questions from Sean, Kent and even Jeremy, on a daily basis. What color are King's eyes? [Orange-brown, and oddly enough, mentioned in only two of the novels!] Is Felice Carter a black woman? [Yes.] Where was Jack Sigler born? [It actually was never mentioned in sixteen stories, so I arbitrarily suggested it'd be Richmond, VA, and Jeremy approved that call.] So there was a need for a story bible or guide, just for the writers. Sean and I had both talked about doing one, a full two years ago, but we never got to it. Eventually Jeremy saw the need for such a beast, too, and not just for the writers but for the readers and fans, as well.

Goes without saying I was best qualified to co-author this one. I've been honored to be an occasional co-author with Jeremy on this series and with these characters that I have grown to love, as if they were my own. I've edited all the books since *Callsign: Queen*, and I've even found myself in the trusted position of consulting on cover designs, interior art, layout, book titles and story direction. Jeremy and his fellow Chess Team co-authors have created a rich, vibrant, complex world full of danger, intrigue, creatures and chaos, and I'm proud to have been a part of it. Thanks, Jeremy. By the end of 2015, there will be twenty books in the Jack Sigler / Chess Team universe (including this guide), and a short story, too! Hopefully this guidebook will help you to keep it all straight.

—Kane Gilmour
Montpelier, VT
February, 2015

ENDGAME

A JACK SIGLER & CHESS TEAM UNIVERSE GUIDEBOOK

CHESS ♟♟ TEAM

Whispers and legends. Tall tales and folklore. Ask any US special forces operator and they'll have heard the stories of a small band of highly efficient rogue operators who can handle things even regular SpecOps soldiers can't. Unnatural things. Hideous, horrible things created in labs by madmen or in antiquity by who-knows-what. *Monsters.* Unstoppable threats that defy the imagination and all sanity. The rumors are rampant, of course, but most operators believe the stories. It's a small community, and as a result, some of the operators know the actual facts.

All the rumors are true.

Formed to handle threats others were powerless to stop—either through inexperience or intervention—and operating outside the purview of the US government, the Chess Team operate out of a seized enemy stronghold in the White Mountains of New Hampshire. Led by a former President of the United States and operating on a budget appropriated from a Pentagon 'Deep Black' account, the team has zero oversight and free rein to right wrongs, defang terrorist threats and crush plots for world domination before they can begin.

Comprised of five special operators from a variety of military backgrounds, each of them—King, Queen, Rook, Bishop and Knight—were made a part of Delta, the US Army's counter-terrorism branch, and later further co-opted into an even more elite group. Termed the 'Delta of Delta,' the Chess Team were answerable only to the President.

Over the years, the team has battled perverse creations of science, terrorist bioweapons plots, deranged megalomaniacs, ancient Nazi schemes, other-dimensional incursions, the re-emergence of villains thought long vanquished, artificial intelligences and full-on revolutions in far-flung locales. Next, they'll face a threat greater than any they've ever known: an insidious and terrifying enemy that just might have the power to destroy the Chess Team forever.

PROLOGUE: UNDISCLOSED

Tom Duncan shifted his weight on the chair, trying to find a comfortable position. The chair was by no means the sort he was used to, but there were times you just had to make do. He'd been waiting an interminable amount of time in the bleak office, but he knew how the government game was played. He could be still and patient for as long as necessary.

The door to the room opened, and a brunette woman in her late thirties entered. She sat down behind the heavy oak desk, opposite Duncan. As a former United States President, he was used to being the one on the commanding side of an oak slab, but this was her office. She was in charge here. The woman wore a cream-colored business suit, with a snug fitting jacket and a white blouse. The double row of pearls around her neck lent her a more dignified and aged look. Duncan knew it was all a part of a calculated style to be accepted by her peers in Washington. Younger women rarely found themselves in positions of great power in the city, so by reminding everyone of an older woman with the pearls, she would command more respect.

Duncan waited for her to seat herself and lay a thick manila folder on the cleared desktop. He remained silent, content to force her to begin the conversation. A subtle but poignant reminder to her that despite her holding an upper hand in the present location, he had years of experience on her. And that the discussion would not go how she expected.

The woman sat quietly, looking Duncan in the eyes. There was no hint of emotion in her smooth pale face and glinting green eyes. Her brown hair was pulled back into a plain pony tail. She wore no earrings and only the faintest hint of make up. Despite the severity of the look, Duncan found her to be quite pretty. But he was far more interested in her presence. Her calm. She, too, appeared to be content to wait out the silence like a Bhutanese monk meditating on the side of a Himalayan peak.

The minutes spun out in silence, until the woman smiled slightly, clearly impressed with Duncan's resolve. Then, at last, she spoke.

"Mr. Duncan, my name is Danielle Rudin. I'm—" she started.

"I know who you are, Ms. Rudin," Duncan interrupted. "You're Dom Boucher's replacement as the Director of the Central Intelligence Agency."

"Interim Director," she corrected. "Despite the approval of President Chambers and the Director of National Intelligence, I doubt the Senate will want a woman in the post for too long."

"Although I disagree with the sentiment, I agree with your assessment. Too bad. Dom always spoke highly of you."

Her smile was slight, but present. Duncan knew that Danielle Rudin had been very loyal to her predecessor, which was probably what had gotten her the job as his temporary replacement.

"So what can I do for you today, Ms. Rudin?" Duncan asked, getting to the meat of things.

"I think we'll find this discussion is really more about what I can do for you, Mr. Duncan." Rudin leaned forward and opened her thick folder, flipping a few pages, pausing on what she read, then flipping through more. "And let me assure you that there are no listening devices in the room. It's just you and me, here, Mr. Duncan."

"Why don't you call me Tom."

She snapped her head up and looked him in the eye. "The formal term of address for a former President is 'Mister,' as you probably know. I can call you Tom, if you prefer..." She paused and let her eyes drop back to her folder before glancing up again. "...unless you'd rather I call you 'Deep Blue.'"

"Tom will be fine." Without showing any reaction on his face, he smiled inwardly. She said it as if it were some big reveal. He knew the woman knew his operational callsign within the Endgame organization, and she knew he knew it. He chalked the melodrama up to working with the CIA.

She read more for a few minutes, flipping pages in the folder. "I think we both know that I would be able to help you out more, if you told me a few more details about your organization."

Duncan looked at her impassively. "I'm sure you can understand my reticence. I need to consider the safety of my people, and your organization is known for having more leaks than a colander."

Duncan was refreshed when Rudin snorted with laughter, in a very unfeminine way. "That's true. All too true. At least Dom tried to do something about that once he was in charge. We both know he was great about keeping secrets. I'm trying to do even better. And as I said, we both know you need my help, so what say we get on with it? Maybe you could tell me a little about your field group, the Chess Team. I already know who they are and some of what they've done. But more details would give me a fuller idea of Endgame's mission statement." She flipped through a few more pages in the folder, then closed it. "I also don't have much information on your organization's personnel. Obviously Dom wasn't your only contact in government. And I already know you had a security cohort from Fort Drum at your disposal. But who else will I be working with?"

Duncan liked the way she said 'working with,' as if she would be speaking to his people directly, when they both knew she would be dealing with him exclusively. It made her sound like she was a part of the team. He wished he'd thought to bring her on board before Boucher had retired. It would have made things a lot easier.

Where to begin? What could he tell her about the Chess Team, the group of operatives he'd put together with the help of a US Army General and the former Director of the CIA, when he himself was still in office as President? They were a special group to combat threats that no other special forces team could handle, answerable only to him, through his voice-modulated and digitally-obscured silhouette as Deep Blue. The name had been an indication of his fondness for chess as well as for his expertise with technology and his approach to strategy. The plan had been simple. Send the team out into the fray, aided and augmented with all the satellite data and computing prowess available to him in his former privileged position. Deep Blue was originally the name of a computer, created by IBM, to battle chessmaster Garry Kasparov across a board of black and white. It had seemed apt at the time, and more so, later, when Duncan appropriated Pentagon black budget funding to set up shop outside of direct government control and oversight.

He had stepped down as President, but he still commanded a stunning amount of US funds and hardware. He had broken more laws than he could count for the greater good, and had risked permanent incarceration for treason even before he had left office, but he and Dom had discussed those risks at length when he had begun, and he wouldn't do anything differently now.

Chess Team made a difference in the world. That was all that mattered.

Duncan scrutinized Rudin across the desk. He knew she, too, had the righteous hunger in her to do the right thing, regardless of the political ramifications, and he respected her for it. He would tell her a bit about the Chess Team operatives now. Just enough for her to do her job and maybe help him more than she thought she would.

CONFIDENTIAL INFORMATION

TOP SECRET

DATE:	2014	ORIGINATOR:	DEEP BLUE

SUBJECT:

OPERATIVES

DATE	ACTION	INITIAL
	ORIGINAL DOCUMENTS	
	UPDATED TO REFLECT	
	TRANSITION OF CALLSIGN: BISHOP	
	FOLLOWING EVENTS IN THE CONGO.	
	DB	

CLASSIFIED

Personnel File 01
Jack Sigler
Callsign: KING
Status: Active

Description:
Height: 5'11"
Weight: 175lbs
Hair: Dark Brown
Eyes: Orange-Brown
Distinguishing marks: Multiple scars all over his body, and a massive 'port-wine stain' birthmark running from his back and down his hip and right leg.

History:
Jack Sigler, callsign: King, was initially a member of the US Army's Delta teams, before being willingly drafted into Chess Team during the Voynich affair (see Missions file: PRIME). At the time he joined the team, he had been a professional soldier for nine years. A former skateboard punk, Sigler joined the Army to get away from a strained home life, after the untimely death of his older sister, Julie. She had perished in a strange Air Force training accident, serving as a role model for him when she was alive, and her death catalyzing his decision to do something important with his life. First the military, and eventually Chess Team became his life.

A shrewd strategic thinker, King was a natural leader. When his team was betrayed by Kevin Rainer in the Iraq desert, King joined with Erik Somers and Stan

Tremblay into a small unit bent on tracking the renegade Rainer down. That assignment led to the formation of Chess Team, with the addition of Zelda Baker, whose loyalty King won over by fighting her to a draw in the boxing ring. Shin Dae-jung, who had been working with Baker, joined the team as a matter of course.

The rest of King's family would have an unusual amount of impact on his life and on Chess Team. During a mission in 2011, Sigler learned that both of his parents were in fact Russian sleeper agents, who had been planted on U.S. soil and eventually abandoned after the Cold War. King had joined the military thinking his father had abandoned the family, when in fact, Peter Sigler (aka Peter Machtcenko) was in Russia, raising a sibling King knew nothing about—Asya Machtcenko, who would one day join Chess Team (see Missions file: OMEGA). Lynn Sigler had kept the secret from her son, and King never would have been the wiser. Then Russia tried to reactivate the Siglers and they felt compelled to fake Lynn's death to avoid scrutiny. The faked death, and the revelation that she was actually alive, couldn't have come at a worse time for King, as an old enemy had returned and attacked Fort Bragg (see Missions file: THRESHOLD).

King is engaged to Dr. Sara Fogg, a CDC epidemiologist. They met on an operation in Vietnam (see Missions file: INSTINCT). The couple also act as parents to King's adopted teen daughter, Fiona, whom he rescued at the end of the same mission. Outside of Chess Team, King maintains a small house in Richmond, VA, and visits with his friend Dr. George Pierce, an archeologist who had been engaged to Julie Sigler (King's older sister) at the time of her death. Although her death had initially strained their relationship, the events in 2009 (see Missions file: PULSE) brought King and Pierce together again, and their friendship has been on solid ground ever since.

During the events in Tunisia in 2013, King was propelled some 2800 years into the past, and he was forced to live those years as an immortal until he caught up to the present. As unbelievable as that sounds (for full info, see Missions file: CONTINUUM), the result has been a more well rounded man, although he has at times shown more circumspection and reticence to place the people he cares about—including his fellow operatives in Chess Team—in harm's way. His experiences through time have only just begun to be documented, but he now possesses a wide array of skills, memories and experiences that have the potential to be useful in the field. He now speaks dozens of languages fluently and possesses a worldly knowledge on most subjects, making him an even better tactician, but one hell of a killjoy at Trivial Pursuit.

Personnel File 02
Zelda Baker
Callsign: QUEEN
Status: Active

Description:
Height: 5'5"
Weight: 115lbs
Hair: Blonde
Eyes: Blue
Distinguishing marks: A brand in the center of her forehead, received at the hands of an enemy. A star shape with a grinning skull in its center—the symbol of the Vietnamese People's Liberation Army *Death Volunteers*. Queen elected to keep the mark instead of opting for plastic surgery. She now wears it as a symbol of her victory over her enemies, but for tactical reasons covers it with her long hair or a headband at times.

History:
As a child, Queen was a bookworm, and despite her stunning good looks she had been constantly teased for being intelligent. She'd become timid and fearful, even more so when her mother died of cancer and the girl's father began beating her. She became consumed by phobias of spiders, mice, heights and enclosed spaces. She was terrified of lightning, and she feared wild animal attacks.

She eventually left home with a man who abused her like her father had done. By the time she lost her first and only son, the man left her, unmarried and with her fears further exaggerated by LSD addiction. She was a train wreck. She checked into a rehab clinic and then enlisted in the U.S. Army.

Her boot camp psychologist diagnosed her with an anxiety disorder brought on by mass phobias and past trauma. He suggested she tackle her fears with intensive aversion therapy. It worked.

She excelled in the Army, and in her free time she took up hunting, base jumping and free-solo rock climbing. Those experiences, combined with her newfound aggression toward fear-inducing situations, helped her excel to the point of legend in the Army. She joined the Army Rangers three years after enlisting—the first woman to ever make it through Ranger school, in a special pilot program for women. She was then recruited into military intelligence, and at the rank of Sergeant, she was assigned a post in Myanmar.

King recruited her directly for the Rainer affair (see Missions file: PRIME), after fighting her to a ten-round standstill in the boxing ring, before General Keasling called a stop to it. From that point on, she was Delta, and the first female member of Chess Team. She quickly became a valued member of the team, often showing a complete lack of fear or inhibition in the field, and excelling at hand-to-hand combat. A fierce and deadly combatant, Queen also has a tender side, as shown by her taking on the role of team medic, and also by her budding relationship with Rook. In all manners, she is a woman transformed from the frail, terrified creature of her past, into a formidable soldier, with a sharp mind and amazing stamina.

She was tortured in Vietnam (see Missions file: INSTINCT), and was very verbal about her need to search for Rook, when he went off-grid the following year, after a failed mission in Russian Siberia. I figured at the time that it was a coping mechanism for her to engage on yet another mission, but ultimately I think she had already developed feelings for Tremblay, and she recognized that it was time for her to recover from the emotional personal baggage of her past, now that she had conquered her fears. While personal relationships within such a tight-knit unit like Chess Team wouldn't have been something I would think was a good thing, in this case, Baker and Tremblay have taken the rough edges off each other, only enhancing their effectiveness in the field.

Personnel File 03
Stan Tremblay
Callsign: ROOK
Status: Active

Description:

Height: 6'0"

Weight: 200lbs

Hair: Dirty blond

Eyes: Blue

Distinguishing marks: Rook, like most of the other members of the team, has taken several grazing bullet wounds to various parts of his body, all of which have left small scars.

History:

Growing up with many sisters on a cow farm in New Hampshire, Rook always knew he wanted to join the service. He quickly distinguished himself and was selected for Delta, first operating under the callsign: Juggernaut, due to his beefy size.

He also distinguished himself in rescuing King, when the latter's former Delta unit was pinned in the desert. Rook has an impulsive need to turn everything into a joke, which initially caused King concern about using him in the field, but the two quickly learned to appreciate the others' talents, and they also became fast friends.

Rook has a pair of signature weapons, which he calls 'the girls.' He acquired a pair of custom-made IMI Desert Eagle Mark XIX Magnum .50 caliber semiautomatic pistols while on an operation in Yemen, prior to becoming involved in the Rainer affair (see Missions file: PRIME). Ever since, he has preferred using the weapons when in the field. In a few cases the weapons have been lost in the field, and we've taken to keeping a locker on *Crescent II* filled with three spare sets of the weapons.

Operating as the team's ordinance specialist and heavy weapons operator (after the demise of Erik Somers; see Missions file: SAVAGE), he has been training the new Bishop in both areas. Known in the field for his use of creative and colorful profanity, Rook is a solid cornerstone of the team, never shying from a challenge, and loyal to a fault.

Consumed with guilt and a growing sense of ennui after a mission in Siberia went sideways (see Missions file: THRESHOLD), he took a well earned but ungranted period of leave, during which he found yet more hardship. Stinging over the loss of soldiers under his direct command, Rook wandered the countryside until an old Russian woman took him in, and ultimately sacrificed her life to keep him safe. Suggesting he find her brother in Severodvinsk, Rook followed the dead woman's wishes, meeting her brother and seeking passage to Norway. On that trip he rescued Asya Machtcenko from gangsters who had abducted her. She would return the favor weeks later, when after becoming embroiled in events in the small town of Fenris Kystby, Rook found himself under attack by the entire town's mind-controlled population. Asya arrived to help him fend them off, and the two later infiltrated

Eirek Fossen's base with Queen's assistance (see Missions file: RAGNAROK).

Aside from his exploits in the field, Rook plays paintball with UNH students, attends sports games, and enjoys films at the cinema. A natural with younger children, he and Fiona (King's adopted daughter) quickly bonded. Rook is presently in a committed relationship with Queen.

Personnel File 04
Erik Somers
Callsign: BISHOP
Status: Missing (presumed K.I.A.)

Description:
Height: 6′4″
Weight: 260lbs
Hair: Black
Eyes: Brown
Distinguishing marks: n/a

History:
Erik Somers was Iranian by birth, born to Faiza Abbasi, the wife of a terrorist recruiter and Anwar Muaddah, the husband's driver. Faiza had arranged for the baby to be smuggled out of the country and adopted by an American Midwest family, shortly before Ayatollah Khomeni's government closed off Iran from the rest of the world.

Somers struggled for much of his life with containing the boiling rage within him. He joined the Marine Corps, before eventually transferring to the Army, and attending Ranger school. He possessed seemingly super-human strength, which should have made him an ideal candidate for Special Forces, but he was initially passed over.

During the Rainer affair (see Missions file: PRIME), he distinguished himself by riding to King's rescue and manhandling an M2 Browning heavy machine gun. King remembered the man and formally requested him for the special Delta unit that was created to chase Rainer down—first in Myanmar, and later in Iran and Europe.

Physically, Somers was a mountain of muscle, and his darker skinned Middle Eastern looks made him all the more intimidating in a post-911 world. He was an intense and quiet figure to begin with, but the Hydra affair (see Missions file: PULSE) resulted in Somers being injected with an experimental regeneration serum by Richard Ridley.

The results made Somers nearly impervious to injury, but with each hit his body took, his psyche slipped ever closer to that of a rage-filled monster. Forced to resort to a variety of strategies from yoga and meditation to aroma therapy, Somers kept his sanity and his cool, until a mission in Vietnam resulted in his acquisition of a crystal that helped to keep his rage in check, without all the New Age remedies. His superhuman ability to withstand damage was an asset to the team. The crystal was eventually lost in a battle with Richard Ridley and his duplicates (see Missions file: THRESHOLD). But the loss of the crystal's restraining powers were felt only briefly, before Ridley removed all traces of Somers's regenerative abilities.

Although the man had endured enough hardships, his darker 'Regen' side resurfaced when he was trapped for an indeterminate amount of time in an alternate dimension as a result of the Dire Wolf affair (see Missions file: RAGNAROK). He later confided he was overcome with rage and actually *ate* a Dire Wolf.

Then, two years later in the Congo, Somers suffered the anguish of seeing his best friend, Shin Dae-jung, horribly disfigured before his eyes, when Knight became the victim of a mortar attack. Somers then had to go up against an army of dinosaurs single-handedly, in a subterranean cavern system that possibly provides evidence of humanity's first major civilization. Taking things into his own hands to stop a French mercenary from destroying the region's natural gas deposits, Somers attacked the woman on the open Lake Kivu with a helicopter, and then swam toward the bottom of the lake to stop a bomb rigged with a depth indicator, from exploding.

We eventually found the device, which Somers dragged to a safer depth before abandoning it. His body was never found, but the depths involved and the amount of time he was under water suggest his death. There are large carnivorous predators in the lake, and if his body drowned and hit the thick silt on the floor of the large body of water, his bones will never be located.

I have been keeping an ear open in Central Africa. There have been rumors of someone loosely matching Somers's description in the jungle. A huge mountain of a man, running naked through a region normally populated by undernourished, slim men. I've tried to track these leads down, but they all go nowhere, and I know it's just wishful thinking on my part.

Erik Somers, the original Bishop, is dead.

Personnel File 05
Shin Dae-jung
Callsign: KNIGHT
Status: Active

Description:
Height: 5′4″
Weight: 120lbs
Hair: Black
Eyes: Black
Distinguishing marks: Left eye missing. Currently replaced by cybernetic mechanism. Scar tissue all around left half of face, due to metal fragment damage.

History:
Knight was perhaps the most well adjusted individual on the team when it was formed. He had a simple and easy childhood, before his parents passed away. When he joined Chess Team during the Rainer affair (see Missions file: PRIME) he was working for military intelligence with Queen in Myanmar, and in his downtime he was pursuing his passions for chasing thrills in extreme sports, and charming women wherever he found them.

Although his pastimes were self indulgent, Knight also has another passion far more selfless. He has just one surviving relative—an aging grandmother, suffering from dementia in a rest home in Florida. He does all he can to visit her often and take care of her in her final days, sparing no expense to obtain top notch care for her.

With sensational scores as a marksman, Knight was the perfect choice for Chess Team, and after the Rainer affair, he thrived on the action. He was the first of the team to battle the Hydra, and he was deep in the thick of it in the Mount Meru affair (see Missions file: INSTINCT). He formed a close friendship with Erik Somers, and while on a mission in China, he once again met Anna Beck, and the two became involved.

Of particular note toward understanding the current state of his psyche were a series of devastating events, each more scarring than the last. During the Fossen affair (see Missions file: RAGNAROK) he was abducted into another dimension. When Erik Somers found him in that otherworldly place and they escaped together, they first compared notes and had each experienced time differently there. According to Knight, he had spent nearly *two years* in that hellish place. Alone, battling Dire Wolves and surviving however he could.

Next, the following year in Tunisia, Knight suffered an intense physical beating at the hands of Darius Ridley. He was in physical therapy for weeks after the battle. Then in the Congo, he lost his eye—and the left half of his face was horribly scarred—in a mortar attack.

Each of these events led him to become more and more driven, as well as more and more taciturn, facing inward to deal with his pain. While he attempts to hide it from the team, his current cybernetic implant causes him excruciating pain. Lewis Aleman is working on a better alternative for Knight. The pain, combined with a cocktail of immunosuppressant drugs to help his body accept the artificial eye are taking their toll on him.

Although these events and their related missions have served to drive Knight closer to Anna, I am concerned for his state of mind. I know his grandmother doesn't have long.

What will one more loss do to him?

Personnel File 06
Asya Machtcenko
Initial Callsign: PAWN
Current Callsign: BISHOP
Status: Active

Description:
Height: 5'6"
Weight: 120lbs
Hair: Wavy black
Eyes: Orange-brown
Distinguishing marks: n/a

History:
Asya Machtcenko came into our lives very suddenly. She was being held aboard the *Songbird*, the vessel Rook had secured passage on to get him out of Russia. He freed her from her captivity, and she later found him in Norway, saving him from a brainwashed village of attackers.

She initially requested Rook's aid in finding her parents, and she would help him with his investigations into the Fossen affair (see Missions file: RAGNAROK). The later revelation that her parents were Peter and Lynn Sigler—King's parents—was a shocker.

Highly proficient in martial arts and ballet, Asya has developed a fighting style that seemed unique to observers. Unless they had also seen King in battle. Trained by her father, who along with her mother was a Soviet spy, she led her parents to believe she would pursue ballet or medicine, but shocked them by enlisting in the Russian army.

She excelled in combat training, but she was unable to gain traction in the military, being passed over for promotions. She left the service and traveled around Russia and abroad, before she was abducted on the streets of Murmansk. After discovering she had a brother, she became a permanent appendage to Chess Team, first as King and Asya scoured the globe searching for their parents, and then later as a support member to the team and eventually as the new callsign: Bishop.

A lover of American films, she has had a very easy transition into life as an American citizen—Endgame pulled some strings with the Department of State on that one. She is a quick study and fiercely intelligent, with a sarcastic wit that immediately ingratiated her with Queen. As competent in the field as she is with her studies, Asya has been a valuable asset in the field. Rook is currently training her in demolitions, and she's shown an aptitude for using heavy weaponry, despite her size.

Note that once they were found in Tunisia, staying as guests of Alexander Diotrephes, the Siglers once again slipped into the wind. The couple, although claiming to be ex-spies, may still be on someone's payroll. It's a very peculiar family, and I fear we might not know all their secrets yet.

Personnel File 07
Tom Duncan
Callsign: DEEP BLUE
Status: Active

Description:
Height: 5'10"
Weight: 165lbs
Hair: Brown (Shaved)
Eyes: Gray
Distinguishing marks: US Army Rangers tattoo, left deltoid.

History: (*Note: this file was written at my behest by Lewis Aleman. –DB)

Thomas Duncan was the youngest President of the United States ever elected. Upon graduating from high school in Massachusetts, he enlisted in the US Army and went to Ranger school. After a distinguished tour in Kuwait during the First Gulf War, he left active service to attend college on a military scholarship, studying military history and economics. He then served his time as an officer, before stepping down and running for senate.

He won in a landslide, and promptly served two terms, becoming known as a proponent of whirlwind reforms on everything from abortion to taxes. He was also a vocal supporter of foreign intervention in just causes.

When he ran for president at the age of forty-two, his veteran status and his efficient approach to politics helped him to sweep the polls. Once in office, he set about a determined policy of harassment for terror organizations, and began building a workable Middle East peace plan.

Behind the scenes, he was looking for military solutions where innocents would not be killed. He wanted to oversee small teams of surgeons who would carefully remove terrorist organizations like cancerous cells from the body, with brutal efficiency. As such, with the assistance of Domenick Boucher at CIA, Major General Michael Keasling on Joint Special Operations Command and myself [former Delta sniper, Lewis Aleman], he set up Chess Team when the Rainer affair was just blowing up (see Missions file: PRIME). At first, King and the other operatives did not know Duncan's identity. They saw only an image on a screen of a silhouetted figure. His keen sense of strategy and amazing connections hinted to Chess Team of his history in the military. Other than that, they knew nothing about the man except that he was their lifeline, their eye in the sky, and he could seemingly mobilize every branch of the military at a whim.

Unable to assist the team on the Brugada affair (see Missions file: INSTINCT), after being struck down as one of the disease's first victims, Mr. Duncan eventually entered the field in Vietnam, and revealed his identity to King and the others.

As the team began to deal with the resurgence of Richard Ridley (see Missions file: THRESHOLD), Mr. Duncan was forced to deal with political attacks from Senator Lance Marrs in Washington, while trying to orchestrate the team's activities globally. In frustration at how the presidency was hindering his efforts for the team instead of helping, he stepped down amidst a scandal created by Marrs, giving the bombastic senator the illusion that he had won, when in fact, Mr. Duncan had orchestrated removing himself from the spotlight for a larger purpose.

Refusing a post-presidency secret service detail and appropriating some Pentagon black budget funding when he stepped down, and with Keasling and Boucher still operating as allies on the inside, Deep Blue set up a larger organization to support Chess Team, called Endgame. He modified a seized lab of Ridley's, in New Hampshire, converting it into a new base of operations for the team, with a full complement of support crew, analysts and soldiers to act as security.

Still in the same level of amazing physical fitness he had kept when in the Rangers, Deep Blue was put through the ringer when the base was attacked on one of his final set-up visits. He and a few others were trapped inside the facility with his security team trapped outside. The individual members of Chess Team were away on various missions and personal agendas at the time. Fighting for his life with Anna Beck and Matt Carrack, Deep Blue was able to fend off a paramilitary team and a small army of genetically mutated salamanders. The clean-up from that fiasco was extensive, but Deep Blue had earned himself an honorary place on the team.

He would see action in the field again during the Dire Wolf incursion (see Missions file: RAGNAROK), but happily returned to his role of overseeing the team remotely via technology, for their next few missions. After the death of Erik Somers in the Congo (see Missions file: SAVAGE), Deep Blue made the bold decision to promote Asya Machtcenko to the role of Bishop on the team.

Constantly straddling a fine line between following the principles of the United States and flaunting the law to accomplish the greater good, Deep Blue is a complicated man with a solid moral compass. He knows that some day he might have to pay the piper for bypassing the chain of command, but until that day, he and his Chess Team will fight the good fight.

CONFIDENTIAL INFORMATION

DATE:	ORIGINATOR:
2014	DEEP BLUE

SUBJECT:

PERSONNEL

DATE	ACTION	INITIAL
	ORIGINAL DOCUMENTS	
	GEORGE PIERCE – OFF THE GRID?	
	FELICE CARTER ALSO REQUIRES	
	MONITORING UNTIL WE KNOW MORE	
	ABOUT HER...AFFLICTION.	
	FIONA'S ABILITIES STILL REQUIRE STUDY.	
	DB	

Support Personnel File 01
Domenick BOUCHER
Status: Retired

Dom Boucher was a top analyst with the CIA when I was a senator, and we became fast friends. He was my first and only choice to be appointed as Director of Central Intelligence when I took office. He helped me to put an end to the former administration's practice of outsourcing the detainment, rendition and interrogation of suspected terrorists. It was partly as a way to restore accountability to the relevant agencies and partly to stop the hemorrhage of taxpayer dollars into what some journalists had taken to calling the 'terror-industrialist complex.'

He was instrumental in helping me form Chess Team during the Rainer affair, and he helped me to step down from the presidency, feeding Marrs the false information he needed to create the scandal that acted as my cover for retreat.

A seemingly unassuming man with a white moustache, Dom has a fiercely intellectual mind, and he's capable of keeping a million balls juggled in the air at once. When we set up Endgame, he continued to offer solid counsel for the team and began to act as a go-between for us and President Chambers, even as Dom was preparing to retire (see Missions file: SAVAGE). Now fully retired, instead of taking up fishing for a hobby, he's spending most of his time with me at Endgame HQ. He's just now learning the ropes here, and I've let him into the sanctum of secrets. All but the Desperado Protocol. Hopefully I'll never have to reveal that to him.

Support Personnel File 02
Major General Michael KEASLING
Status: Deceased

I first met Brigadier General Michael Keasling shortly before the Rainer affair. When I had to fire Roger Collins as commander of the Joint Special Operations Command (JSOC), a task force commissioned with making sure U.S. special ops weaponry and tactics were the best in the world, I rapidly appointed Mike, and got him a promotion to Major General. Another mustached friend, Mike was the guy in the room who was on the phone ordering what you needed before you thought to ask for it. I always liked that about him.

Along with Dom Boucher, Mike helped me set up Chess Team, consulting on the individual members. While he bristled at the team's lack of military bearing (especially Rook's) he understood the need for a tight, cohesive unit, and the tradition of Delta shooters not following certain military rules.

The General could always be counted on to bring military assistance when the team needed it—even after I stepped down from office. He was on the scene in New York during the Dire Wolf affair (see Missions file: RAGNAROK), and when King and I leapt off a gigantic collapsing skyscraper to a waiting helicopter with a net, Keasling and his men were unfortunately under the plummeting debris. It was only a matter of time until we lost someone, but I always thought it would be a member of the field team, and not one of my closest friends working in a support capacity. At the end, despite his gruff exterior, he was quite fond of each member of the team, and as I discovered at his memorial, he was well loved by thousands.

Support Personnel File 03
Lewis ALEMAN
Status: Active
(*Note: This file is cipher-locked, and will be opened
for Lewis only upon my death or capture, when
I don't regularly enter the pass-code.)

His lean body stands at six-two, and he used to run
track. Aleman was a Delta sniper attached to King's unit
in Iraq during the Rainer affair. His right hand was
damaged and broken in that battle, and while it spelled
the end of his days as a military sniper, I had other uses
for him, as I was setting up Chess Team.

Unlike many snipers, he also had a keen interest in
science and technology. He seemed part machine, as he
interfaced with computer systems, hacking networks
and retaining information with more reliability than a
hard drive. He liked to say that he could do the work of
two NSA supercomputers, and no one doubted it.

There would be times as the team's eyes and ears
when I wouldn't be able to be in two places at once.
That was when Lew would come in. Eventually, the two
of us worked as a finely tuned unit, providing intel and
computer support to the team when they were in the
field. Lew really stepped up his help during the Dire
Wolf incursion (see Missions file: RAGNAROK), and he's
become an invaluable part of the organization and a
good friend. If anything ever happens to me, Lewis will
need to take my place. I have faith that he can do the job
well. I just hope it never comes to that.

Support Personnel File 04
Anna Beck
Initial Callsign: PAWN
Current Callsign: BLACK ZERO
Status: Active

Anna Beck joined the Army after high school, and immediately after her term of service she found herself working for mercenary security group Gen-Y, protecting Richard Ridley's Manifold Genetics installations. She was at the Gamma facility in Peru when a security leak led to Ridley abandoning the lab.

She was then assigned to the Alpha lab in New Hampshire, and after having her eyes opened to what Manifold was doing, she assisted King and Knight in infiltrating the facility, and later fought with them against the Hydra and against Ridley himself, using the callsign given to all temporary assets in the field: Pawn. At the end of the Hydra affair (see Missions file: PULSE), she slipped away.

She didn't pop back up on Endgame's radar again until the Huangdi affair in China, when she and Knight teamed up in the field, and later in their personal lives. I offered her a position with the then newly-formed Endgame organization, and she quickly distinguished herself when a Gen-Y assault team came knocking, trapping us in the base. After that mess and the craziness of the Dire Wolf affair (see Missions file: RAGNAROK), where we lost a significant number of support personnel, I promoted her to my personal bodyguard and the head of Endgame's intelligence gathering.

Support Personnel File 05
Matt Carrack
Initial Callsign: WHITE ONE
Current Callsign: WHITE ZERO
Status: Deceased

Initially designated White One, Matt was the leader of Endgame's first security force. He was relentless in his attempts to penetrate the base after I was locked in it, when the Gen-Y team assaulted the base, just before we made it operational (see Missions file: DEEP BLUE). Working in tandem with Anna Beck, Matt helped me quell that incursion and deal with pest control.

As a trained 10th Mountain Division soldier from Fort Drum, Matt was a lethal special forces soldier and a world-class rock climber. He was also a sharp and effective leader. Unfortunately, the rest of his team was killed by death traps and the mutated salamander infestation.

After the death of Lori Stanton, who I had appointed as my administrative assistant, Matt took over her role as White Zero, fulfilling Lori's job and acting as head of security for Endgame. He trained a new squad of 10th Mountain troops to act as the organization's protectors, but unfortunately many of them, and Matt himself, perished in battle in Norway, during the Dire Wolf affair (see Missions file: RAGNAROK). He was a good soldier, and I had plans for him joining the field team should anything happen to the five primaries. If he had lived, Matt would likely be the new Bishop today.

Support Personnel File 06
George PIERCE, Ph.D.
Status: Active

Dr. Pierce, an expert on Greek antiquity, was once engaged to be married to King's older sister, Julie. When she died in a military training exercise, Pierce and King grew apart. When Pierce was called to Nazca to consult on the Hydra find, he called King in to act as security for the site, but they both quickly found themselves swept up into Richard Ridley's maniacal schemes.

Experimented upon by Ridley and his chief scientist, Dr. Pierce's skin was turned scaly and green, his body filled with the first of Ridley's Hydra DNA-tinged regenerative serums. Endgame was eventually able to cure Pierce, but I wonder about the psychological damage of the incident.

Despite his trauma, once inducted into Chess Team's chaotic world, Dr. Pierce became a treasured resource during the mother tongue affair (see Missions file: THRESHOLD) and during the BlueLight affair with King (see Missions file: UNDERWORLD). Pierce practically became a full member of the team during the next few missions, before he returned to his archeological research in Europe.

While I don't keep constant tabs on the man, I have noticed him disappearing for prolonged periods, since King's journey through time and the conclusion of the Carthage battle (see Missions file: OMEGA). At first I thought Pierce might be visiting his drug addict brother in New

York, but they haven't seen each other since the start of the BlueLight incident. I'm curious if George is perhaps moonlighting for the Greek National Intelligence Service. Dom assures me he isn't doing any spying for or against our side. Still worth watching.

Of peculiar note, is that despite not being blood relatives, Pierce has the same orange-flecked brown eyes that King and Asya have. Makes me wonder if somewhere in his lineage, George has connections to Alexander Diotrephes.

Support Personnel File 07
Sara Fogg, M.D.
Initial Callsign: PAWN
Current Callsign: JETT
Status: Active

Dr. Sara Fogg is another unexpected ally to our cause. She joined the team as a temporary Pawn in Vietnam, during the Brugada outbreak (see Missions file: INSTINCT). A star disease detective for the Centers for Disease Control and Prevention, she was the best qualified to assist the team in finding a cure.

King quickly noted her unique ability to detect danger before the others. He later discovered it was a result of her affliction with a rare Sensory Processing Disorder, which scrambles her senses and sometimes heightens them. Although normally a liability in her line of work, on that mission, her being able to smell something before the others could hear it was a huge asset.

After the Brugada outbreak, she was directly involved in the elephant graveyard incident in Ethiopia (see Missions file: CALLSIGN: KING) and the mess at the Louvre in Paris, when King faced off against Graham Brown for the third time (see Missions file: BLACKOUT). Sara helped at Endgame HQ during the Dire Wolf affair, as well.

Sara and King became romantically entangled by the end of the Brugada problem, and she and King became engaged to be married a few years later. They jointly parent Fiona Lane-Sigler.

Support Personnel File 08
Fiona Apserkahar Lane-Sigler
Callsign: PROFESSOR
Status: Active

Young pre-teen Fiona Lane was the last surviving member of her people, after the massacre at the Siletz Reservation in Oregon. King, investigating that event, and having missed the destruction by minutes, found her sleeping in the back seat of his car after he investigated the ruins. Initially thinking George Pierce had sent him to Siletz, he found the girl with a note pinned to her, ostensibly from Alexander Diotrephes. Yet, as King tells me, it turned out he was the one responsible for saving her, after his journey through time, and before he rejoined the team in Carthage. So yes, there were two Jack Siglers in Oregon that day. (See Missions files OMEGA and CONTINUUM for better explanations of this strange event).

As the last living speaker of her tribe's language, and a general student of linguistics, she was a natural to pick up some of the phrases in the mother tongue that Richard Ridley had mastered (see Missions file: THRESHOLD). Thankfully, she claims to have forgotten the actual words of that language, but when she and Sara were in Paris during the Blackout affair, she discovered a new ability to hear inanimate objects speak and even sing to her. She was instrumental in putting a raging black hole back into a form of inert sleep. There is definitely more to this young woman than meets the eye.

Of note, Fiona is an insulin-dependent diabetic. She also has a tattoo the size of a quarter on the back of her right hand, the emblem of the Herculean Society. She was tattooed without her permission, during the mother tongue affair, when Alexander Diotrephes abducted her to keep her safe from Ridley. While she talked about having the tattoo removed initially, after King's journey through time, she opted to keep the symbol, accepting it as a part of who she is. Also of note, as the last surviving member of her tribe, she is due to inherit the rights to the Siletz land when she turns eighteen.

INTERLUDE: EXCHANGE

Danielle Rudin sat back in her chair, as a young man with a shellacked Washington haircut brought in a tray with a carafe of piping hot coffee and mugs. He wore a slightly loose gray suit, but Duncan's trained eye easily spotted the concealed pistol in the man's armpit. The man set the tray down without a word and left the room.

Without asking, Rudin poured Duncan a mug of the brew, adding his cream and no sugar, before sliding the ceramic mug across the desk's surface to him. In addition to picking up on the fact that she knew his coffee preference, he was amused by the red and blue seal of the President of the United States on the white mug. The seal was outlined in inlaid gold. She'd picked it up just for him.

As Rudin prepared her own plain white mug, Duncan sat back, breathing in the aroma of the fine coffee, and thinking about where she would likely steer the conversation next. *To our enemies, most likely. And the missions we've undertaken to keep this country safe from threats the American people can't even imagine, let alone combat with conventional forces.*

Rudin surprised him by unbuttoning her jacket and slinging it over the back of her chair. The white blouse with the pearls was a carefully tailored hybrid between stodgy school marm and the sexy librarian look. She leaned back and sipped her own coffee, before smiling at him.

"That's really all you want to say about your people? Nothing more to add? All you've really told me is what I already knew."

"Isn't it your job to already know things before people tell you about them?" Duncan countered.

Rudin snorted again. "Touché."

She leaned forward, setting the mug down on the table with exactly the right amount of force without looking at it—the seasoned moves of a Washington professional. Coffee was the lifeblood, and being able to multitask was as essential as using a hammer was for a carpenter. She flipped through the manila folder on her desk again.

"Anything you want to tell *me* about my people in there?" Duncan said. "Anything more to add?"

Rudin glanced up, but the smile on her face was less congenial and showing a faint trace of the predator. "What can you tell me about Richard Ridley and Manifold Genetics?" she countered.

Duncan sighed. "Dear Lord, what can't I tell you about that psychopath." He acted exhausted, but he was feeling fresh. It was all part of the game. "I suppose you want to know more about the other threats Chess Team faced, as well?"

"It would be helpful," Rudin said, the congenial smile fixed firmly in place again.

"Allowing you to see the good we've accomplished?" Duncan asked, his own smile in place.

"And any damage you've done."

At least she didn't say the *damage you've done. She's giving me the benefit of the doubt.*

That one word—'any'—might be all the leverage he would need in this conversation, and in all those that would follow. His smile broadened as he realized that the woman was offering more help than he'd thought she would.

"So it's Ridley you really want to hear about, is it?"

Rudin waved her hand in the air. "Oh, I'd like to hear about Weston, too, and—" she glanced down at the folder, "—Graham Brown, and the events that nearly decimated Paris four years ago. Not to mention that mess with the Norwegian that wrecked a good portion of the planet. Most of the affected cities are still rebuilding."

Duncan scowled at the memory. He wasn't likely to forget. The battle in New York had cost him a good friend and had nearly cost him his own life, as well.

He reached carefully over with his own coffee mug and set it on the desk, his eyes never leaving the cup. With his newly limited mobility, it was necessary. Gone were the days when he could carelessly fling a cup of joe without looking, as Rudin had done.

"I'm not sure going over old cases will help me out with what I need today," Duncan said, looking Rudin in the eye and gauging her real interest in helping him. It was there all right. He had always been good at reading people, and he was reading her correctly now. She wasn't supposed to help him. She'd be breaking dozens of laws doing so. But she saw the results Chess Team achieved, and her interest was clear.

Maybe he would be able to use her more than he had hoped. Maybe she would even be an ally, a solid replacement for the functions Boucher had been able to fulfill when he had been the Director of the CIA.

Duncan would tell her just enough. It was need-to-know, after all. He'd tell her about the threats, the creatures and the madmen. He'd tell her about the missions Chess Team had undertaken—although he would keep it all in broad terms. About how Chess Team had saved the world from the extinction of all life, by fighting monstrosities in a cave in France. About how one crazy megalomaniac had hoped to secure immortality for himself with an army of regenerating soldiers. About weaponized plagues, rogue computer geniuses, pocket-sized black holes, the failed coup d' état in the Congo and about all hell breaking loose in North Africa with the recently discovered Colossus of Rhodes. He would tell her about the dimensional invasion that snatched large gouges out of cities around the globe.

He'd tell her just enough for her to realize how many times Chess Team had saved her bacon and the planet's. Just enough to sink the hook in deep. If things didn't go his way and he didn't think he was going to get what he wanted out of the arrangement with Rudin, he'd either unveil his trump card now, or wait until she was replaced with a permanent Director and use it on him. The Central Intelligence Agency used to be under Duncan's command. He knew exactly how to manipulate them, if it became necessary.

First as a Ranger, then as a government servant, later as President and finally as the head of Endgame,

Duncan had a wealth of experience with the twin worlds of intelligence and politics. He knew two things were essential to survive: sensitive and damaging knowledge the other side didn't know you possessed, and the uncompromising willingness to play dirty.

He'd spent years acquiring the former, but he'd always had the latter.

CONFIDENTIAL INFORMATION

| DATE: | 2014 | ORIGINATOR: | DEEP BLUE |

SUBJECT:

THREATS

DATE	ACTION	INITIAL
	ORIGINAL DOCUMENTS	
	NEEDS UPDATING!	
	MARRS.	
	MANO.	
	RED QUEEN.	
	WHAT IS THE CERBERUS GROUP?	
	DB	

FOR YOUR EYES ONLY

Threat File 01
Richard RIDLEY
Status: Dormant

This bald, blue-eyed geneticist and businessman was a student of antiquity, and excelled at hiring better and crazier geneticists than himself. As we later came to discover, this savvy foe started a world-wide billion-dollar company called Manifold Genetics. Their aims were simple—to perfect human regeneration, so that Ridley might grant himself immortality. Then with his newfound longevity, he would seek out the power to create with the mother tongue (see Missions file: THRESHOLD) and the power to destroy with the fabled Chest of Adoon (see Missions file: OMEGA).

We first stumbled across Ridley's dabbling in ancient and powerful things during the Rainer affair, even though we didn't know at the time that he had backed Dr. Katherine Geller's dig in China, which released the al-Tusi *Urghan*. We first learned of him when his soldiers abducted George Pierce and got their hands on the desiccated head of the Lernaean Hydra.

Although he was defeated in New Hampshire, the man had dosed himself with his new regenerative serum, and survived a fall from a helicopter. He resurfaced two years later, murdering the last speakers of the world's ancient languages and wielding the mother tongue—and an ability to bring the inanimate to life. King managed to decapitate the man at the end of that battle, before he was buried under tons of sand and rubble.

Or so we thought.

While we were busy cleaning up the remnants of the man's varied enterprises and allies around the world, Alexander Diotrephes had kept Ridley imprisoned in an inhumane but uniquely designed set of cages, torturing the man for information (see Missions file: OMEGA). Although Ridley escaped with the help of his created duplicates, and he caused all manner of havoc when he animated the long lost statue of the Colossus of Rhodes, King eventually defeated the man once again, with an ingenious trap. Once again beheaded, King cauterized the man's neck and buried his dehydrated head under the very same stone in Nazca that kept the Hydra secure for over twenty-four centuries. Hopefully, we have seen the last of Richard Ridley.

Threat File 02
Alexander DIOTREPHES
Status: Unknown
Cross-Reference: Herculean Society

I had a difficult time deciding whether I wanted to label Alexander a 'Threat,' but ultimately, this was the place for him. This curly, black-haired man with dark brown eyes constantly rode the line between ally and foe. Standing at six foot five, it's easy to see why people in the ancient world believed him to be superhuman or a god. I still have a hard time swallowing the idea that he was the Hercules of legend, though.

Chess Team first ran afoul of the man in Gibraltar, when they were searching for a way to stop the Hydra that Richard Ridley had unleashed (see Missions file: PULSE). He was less than welcoming to Queen and Rook, receiving them with a story about how the Herculean Society was founded to protect history and its artifacts. While he personally resorted to deception and threats, he ultimately provided them with the serum the team used to dispatch the Hydra, and which our Endgame scientists used to cure George Pierce. Supposedly, Alexander was the one who had buried the Hydra's head in Nazca in the first place.

When the team returned to Gibraltar, the man and his people had packed up and left. We thought we'd seen the end of him until the Siletz massacre, when King found Fiona with a note he initially thought was from Alexander (it later turned out to be from King himself). Then during the mother tongue affair, Alexander rescued and then abducted Fiona, taking her to Rome in an attempt to keep her safe (even branding her with a tattoo, marking her as under his protection). Ridley's golems made short work of the base, and Fiona was taken, regardless. Chess Team worked with the man to find and stop Ridley once again. Fiona was saved, and we thought Ridley was dead. Alexander made it through that mission with reluctant assistance and half truths (for instance, he lied to King about having no children).

Then King ran into Alexander again during the Paris blackout—although Sara and Fiona actually met up with Alexander first. He helped Fiona to stop the black hole from swallowing the city, even if she didn't do it the way he had wanted.

It was only after King received another note from 'Alexander' (again actually from himself) that the team went after the man, thinking him a threat to King's parents, and to the planet, when Ridley's duplicates revealed that he possessed not only his own regenerative abilities, but also the dimensional technology from Norway (see Missions file: RAGNAROK) and the piece of rubble from Paris containing the black hole. With the revelation that Alexander was keeping Ridley prisoner, so he could obtain the mother tongue, as well, Alexander became Chess Team enemy # 1.

While I can ultimately forgive the man many of his actions because his motivation was good-hearted—he was trying to travel back in time to save the life of his true love—his methods left much to be desired. As illustrated by him abducting King through time, to use King in his schemes. A *one-way trip* through time. As

King came to find out, he was one of Alexander's descendents, and Alexander was not even human, but a man from another dimension. Successful in their mission to save the life of Acca Larentia, Alexander's wife, the man and his spouse journeyed to his home dimension, leaving King stranded in the past, to live through 2800 years of history before he could rejoin us here in the present.

We have no idea where it was that Alexander went, or whether he will ever return. Also of note, we have no way of tracking all of his descendents. We also have no idea what became of the Herculean Society after Alexander's departure.

Threat File 03
Lernaean HYDRA
Status: Dormant

This creature is a tough one to write about because its origins are shrouded in ancient history and myth. But there's no disputing the fact that it was real, and its head was buried under a huge stone in Nazca, Peru. Richard Ridley's people got control of the desiccated head and brought it first to a lab in Peru, then to one in the Atlantic Ocean and finally to New Hampshire, where it was unintentionally re-hydrated.

The creature eventually grew to full size during the battle, having nine heads, each with fins, resembling dragon heads. It also had an insatiable hunger for human flesh. The creature was able to rapidly regenerate from any injuries it received. If it wasn't for the serum Alexander provided, we might not have been able to stop the beast. Its remains are in a secure concrete bunker, ten miles under the Kansas plains, guarded round the clock by a team of soldiers loyal directly to Endgame.

Threat File 04
Anthony WESTON, Ph.D.
Status: Deceased

Weston was a cryptozoologist who disappeared in 1995. The man encountered the Nguoi Rung, a race of devolved Neanderthals that had survived the ages in the densely jungle-covered interior of Vietnam. Because their males had died out, the 'Old Mothers' forcibly mated with Weston, creating a new race of Hybrids. Weston served as the Alpha in the community and treated his hybridized offspring as his children. The new race grew to two thousand strong.

The man cared for his brood to the point of insanity, and when Chess Team encountered him, looking for a cure to the Brugada outbreak (see Missions file: INSTINCT), he attempted to kill Erik Somers. Aware of the worldwide potential for calamity, he insisted that the Nguoi Rung and his new race of Hybrids were more important than Homo Sapiens, and he did everything he could to stop Chess Team. King ultimately shot and killed the man.

Threat File 05
HYBRIDS
Status: Unknown

After Anthony Weston stumbled into the last remnants
of the Nguoi Rung in Vietnam, the surviving females of
the species mated with him to create a new hybridized
race. Part devolved Neanderthal and part homo sapiens,
the Hybrids grew to full size (approximately five foot tall
and covered in fur) in just two short years.

The tribe grew to over two thousand, and they
excelled in their environment, moving rapidly through
trees overhead, and possessing the strength of silverback
gorillas. Although they were strong, most of them were
either not particularly intelligent—or else Weston had
intentionally deprived them of certain things in their
education.

At the end of the Brugada event, the team was
forced to flee Vietnam, and Rook insisted that the
remaining Hybrids (and the remaining Old Mothers) be
left in peace. A year later, he returned to Mount Meru to
discover that Red, the Old Mother who had taken a
shine to him, had been killed by Ridley's forces as they
scoured the globe executing those last living speakers of
ancient tongues. It is unknown if any other Old Mothers
or Hybrids survived the attack.

Threat File 06
RED
Status: Deceased

Red was the most aggressive of the Old Mothers at Mount Meru (see previous entries on Weston and the Hybrids, and also the Missions file: INSTINCT). After she and the other Old Mothers—devolved Neanderthal women in a tribe whose males had all died out—forced their way on Anthony Weston and revived the species, he and the Hybrids shunned the more violent Old Mothers.

When Chess Team arrived on site, she wanted Rook as her new Alpha male, and to placate her, he promised he would be her consort. When the mountain was destroyed, and most of the Hybrids and Old Mothers were killed, she grudgingly let him go with the team.

A year later, she was the last surviving victim of an attack on the mountain by Richard Ridley's forces, and died when Rook arrived, after saving his life from a Ridley-animated crystal golem. Due to the nature of the urgency of the mission, Rook departed immediately, but Red supposedly fell right next to the same unusual crystals that cured Erik Somers of his Regen rage the previous year. I wonder if the crystals would have had any effect on her seemingly fatal injuries. It wouldn't be the first time we had faced a resurrected foe. When time permits, I plan to send a small science team back to Mount Meru.

Threat File 07
GOLEMS
Status: Dormant

The only thing worse than a regenerating foe was an inanimate one. When Richard Ridley gained the use of the mother tongue, the human protolanguage from before the Tower of Babel story, also called 'the language of God,' he gained the ability to grant life to inanimate things— stone, crystal and bone—and also to mutate living things.

Chess Team faced Ridley's stone rhino golem in Fort Bragg, which devastated most of the base. They also fought an army of golem skeletons in Guatemala, a creature formed from the very rocks of Stonehenge in England, huge mutated sand skinks and desert mantises, living statues and a few years later, Ridley's *pièce de résistance*: an animated 300-foot tall Colossus of Rhodes, which had been sleeping peacefully under the water off the Tunisian coast.

While Chess Team ultimately put down some of these monstrosities, just as many of them ceased their attacks and returned to their dormant material, when Ridley was done with them. It remains to be seen whether they are now inert because of Ridley's demise, or whether some life exists in them somehow, and they are waiting to rise again one day.

Threat File 08
Felice CARTER, Ph.D.
Status: Unknown

Dr. Carter might be the most dangerous person alive. A geneticist working for an offshoot of Manifold in Africa, she somehow quantum entangled with the 'spirit' of a woman thousands of years old and with every other living person on the planet. As a result, she has the ability to simply switch off the evolution of anyone at will—or in some cases involuntarily.

Dr. Sara Fogg hypothesized that the human race had been exposed to a retrovirus that was connected with the pivotal event in the evolution of human consciousness. Carter can simply turn off the genome responsible for that human sentience.

We only even found out about Carter because of Fogg being called in to consult on Carter's case. Chess Team encountered her again in the Congo, when Erik Somers and Knight found her science camp attacked in the jungle. She helped with the science on the extremophile found under Lake Kivu (see Missions file: SAVAGE), and she had seemed to be building a rapport—if not an actual attraction to—Erik Somers, before his death. The woman can now supposedly keep her ability in check. But what if she can't?

Perhaps of even greater concern than Carter turning malicious or losing control are these two questions: What happens if someone gets their hands on her DNA, and what happens to the human race if Felice Carter dies?

Threat File 09
Darius RIDLEY
Status: ~~Two-Dimensional~~
   Deceased
   (Lewis: That sort of thing is not acceptable.
   Changed to 'Deceased.' D.B.)
   [Sorry, Boss. L.A.]

Darius Ridley was Richard Ridley's brother, and he had apparently angered his brother and been sent to oversee a small, mostly unimportant lab in the Ukraine as punishment. The lab was under the town of Pripyat—famous for being deserted as a result of the Chernobyl nuclear power plant meltdown.

When Queen investigated the site, seeking the lab, which we hoped was as deserted as the town above it, she encountered the man and his strange fascination with turning an abandoned amusement park into a series of death traps (see Missions file: CALLSIGN: QUEEN). In an epic hand-to-hand fight, Queen bit the man's ear off, but he escaped the destruction of the lab to torment the team years later, when he attempted to take out both Chess Team and his brother with one move, backed up by an army of mercenaries. His plans quickly fell apart, and he met his unfortunate end on the under-side of the Colossus of Rhodes's foot, as Ridley had the creature rampaging around the ruins of Carthage.

Threat File 10
Edmund KISS
Status: Deceased

Edmund Kiss was a Nazi scientist who set up an Ahnenerbe group in Norway to conduct all manner of hideous experiments. One of the results of those tests was turning himself into a yeti-like clawed creature capable of communicating with wolves. He survived for decades, unnoticed, and he continued to nest in the abandoned lab adjacent to the active lab of his son—Eirek Fossen.

When livestock began to go missing in the small town of Fenris Kystby and Rook happened to be passing though, he hunted the creature and eventually learned the truth—that Kiss was the creature. Mortally wounded, the beast encouraged Rook to finish it off, but not before leaving behind a file of information that tipped Rook off to the kind of dangerous dimensional experiments the son—Fossen—was conducting nearby.

Threat File 11
Dawoud ABBASI
Status: Deceased

Abbasi was, thankfully, one of the team's more mundane
threats, and *not* Erik Somer's biological father. Somers
was initially led to believe that Abbasi, a recruiter for
several terror organizations in Iran and Yemen, was in
fact his birth father.

That turned out not to be the case (see Missions file:
CALLSIGN: BISHOP), and Somers was able to stop the
man from acquiring and selling a highly dangerous
biological weapon, Ergot-B, but not before Abassi, in a
last ditch effort, swallowed some, turning into a rage-
filled, mindless killing machine. Erik Somers was able to
kill the man before he created too much chaos.

Threat File 12
HUANGDI
Status: Unknown, Presumed Deceased

There were days when I thought we'd never hear the last of Richard Ridley. A handful of the man's scientists escaped New Hampshire with Hydra DNA, and Philip Cho attempted to recreate the creature by mixing its DNA with a human test subject. The result was Huangdi, a nearly unstoppable, regenerating creature the size of a dump truck, that looked like a cross between a man and a dragon.

As if that wasn't enough, Philip Cho, addled on drugs, injected himself after mistakenly thinking he had perfected the serum. He turned into something even nastier, but Knight and Anna Beck were able to escape the town in China, leaving behind a self-destruct mechanism at the base and a thermobaric bomb, which together, we hope, obliterated all traces of the Cho-monster and Huangdi.

Threat File 13
GEN-Y
Status: Disbanded/Deceased

Gen-Y was a private mercenary security force in the exclusive employ of Manifold Genetics. They tended to hire violent and young ex-military, and they were a serious force that Chess Team encountered first in Peru, then in Ridley's Atlantic base and then again in New Hampshire.

Long after we thought Ridley was no longer a threat, smaller factions of Gen-Y presented problems in Europe and even right here at Endgame HQ, when Martin Damien led a strike team here to recover DNA and computer data. As far as we know, most of the organization is dead or disbanded.

Although all of Ridley's sites that we knew of have been cleaned up now, the possibility that some Gen-Y soldiers are out there somewhere holding a grudge, keeps me up at night. They had knowledge of all of Ridley's sites and security protocols. It's the unknown threat that always poses a problem for Chess Team—and for the world.

Threat File 14
Graham BROWN/BRAINSTORM
Status: Unknown, Presumed Deceased

Graham Brown was a serious thorn in King's side (see Missions files: CALLSIGN: KING, UNDERWORLD and BLACKOUT). An Atlantic City gambler with an almost machine-like ability for computations and probabilities, he was able to masquerade as a sentient computer network called Brainstorm for many years, securing government, intelligence and military contracts.

Keenly interested in energy research, Brown was involved in the elephant graveyard affair, seizing the Manifold research that connected to the virus that initiated Felice Carter's devastating abilities. He was also behind the BlueLight Technologies scheme with the US Army in Arizona, and he fell victim to another man's scam in Paris, resulting in the blackout and the near destruction of the city and the planet by a black hole.

Getting sucked through the black hole was too good a fate for him. Unfortunately, we cannot confirm his demise.

Threat File 15
Eirek FOSSEN & FENRIR
Status: Unknown, Presumed Deceased

Fossen was the most dangerous kind of fanatic—a religious one. Only in his case, he worshiped a creature from another dimension that he thought was the giant wolf from Norse mythology—Fenrir. In actuality, the creature was a massive mound of white goo with cloudy-skinned sacks that dangled from its torso like pendulous breasts. The creature ruled over another dimension where all human life had been extinguished, and it had its heart set on invading our world.

Fossen was a scientist who followed the whispers from the creature, constructing a dimensional portal to allow his mistress through to our world—but he was inadvertently opening portals all across the globe that were eating cities and disgorging armies of Dire Wolves (see Missions file: RAGNAROK).

King was able to stop both Fossen and his goddess, crashing a 500-million dollar stealth aircraft through the portal, and depositing a nuclear device in the other dimension, before he slipped back and we disabled the doorway. While the fates of Fossen and Fenrir are unconfirmed, we can hope they are both glowing a bright, nuclear green in whatever passes for hell in that dimension.

CONFIDENTIAL INFORMATION

DATE: 2014	ORIGINATOR: DEEP BLUE
SUBJECT:	**MISSIONS**

DATE	ACTION	INITIAL
	ORIGINAL DOCUMENTS	
	NOTE: OBTAIN MORE BACKGROUND ON KING'S EXPERIENCES. LOOSE ENDS? POTENTIAL BLOWBACK ON TEAM?	
	DB	
	SEE NEW FILE: GUARDIAN CROSS-REF: CONTINUUM	
		LA

FOR YOUR EYES ONLY

Mission 00
Designate: PRIME

PRIME was where it all began.

It was only after the fact, that we discovered the problem began in Yunnan Province, China, when Dr. Katherine Geller unearthed a tomb containing an organism not entirely unlike the Black Death. She also uncovered a peculiar device designed by Nasir al-Tusi in the 13th century, in Baghdad. Al-Tusi and his fellow scholars had discovered a deadly connection between nature and sound, and they had constructed a device that when used in the correct place, where the harmonics were properly amplified and connected with the Earth's lines of force—a place called the *Prime*—they could create new kinds of life. Or destroy them.

Apparently a Chinese general confiscated the device and brought it back to China. The theory is that he inadvertently created the plague that ravaged Asia and Europe in the 14th century. But the unveiling of the device in 2005 was what started the chain of events that brought Chess Team together. Only years later did we realize the dig and the subsequent events were funded by Richard Ridley.

In Iraq, the Delta team to which King was attached at the time, captured two al-Awda couriers and several documents. The documents suggested that terrorists were very close to deciphering the Voynich manuscript, which they believed would assist them in the creation of biological weapons. The Voynich was an undeciphered, illustrated codex written in an unknown language.

Dating from the middle ages, it had been puzzling scholars and cryptographers alike for centuries. Now with a new lead on the subject, the CIA scrambled Dr. Sasha Therion, one of their finest cryptographers and a Voynich specialist, to investigate the documents King's team had acquired. They appeared to lead to a location where the manuscript was supposedly in the process of being deciphered by al-Awda. But the whole thing turned out to be a ruse, orchestrated by Kevin Rainer, King's former commanding officer. Rainer was in the employ of Richard Ridley, and he set up the elaborate scheme to draw Therion out into the open. He promptly abducted her, leaving King's unit in the desert and besieged by insurgents.

General Keasling sent additional Ranger and Delta teams in to rescue King, his friend and fellow operator Daniel Parker and Lewis Aleman, who had been injured in the fight. Among those who came to the rescue were Erik Somers and Stan Tremblay. Keasling sent this combined group to chase Rainer down in Myanmar (formerly known as Burma), where Zelda Baker and Shin Dae-jung were already on site, staking out an organ-harvesting organization that was funneling money to terror groups in the Middle East. After an epic mixed martial arts fight between King and Baker, King drafted her and Shin into his new unit.

Rainer's people clearly believed al-Tusi's unearthed organ could be used to code-break the Voynich manuscript, but Therion's research in Myanmar was interrupted when King's team attacked the complex. The organ was destroyed in the battle, but Rainer escaped with Therion in tow. King's group was pinned down by an army of 'frankensteins'—a group of child soldiers that had been experimented upon. They were composed of multiple skin, limb and even mechanical grafts, and functioned as mindless soldiers. King's group escaped, battling 'Buru' along the way. Knight and Bishop later described these creatures as alligator-like, komodo dragon-like jungle animals.

With the commitment of Keasling, Dom Boucher and Lewis Aleman, I formally established King's group as Chess Team, and began using my callsign of Deep Blue. Queen had nabbed Therion's laptop containing her notes on the Voynich manuscript and on the organ. King's friend Parker was able to hack the device with Aleman's assistance, and we deduced that Rainer would take Therion to the Maragheh Observatory in Iran, seeking al-Tusi's original notes on the creation of the organ. After another skirmish, a car chase and a hair-raising extraction of Therion and Chess Team via the Fulton STARS Skyhook system using a prototype stealth plane later christened *Crescent*, Parker and Therion were able to crack the Voynich code and determine the location of the *Prime.*

King and Parker set up a plan to delude Therion into thinking Parker had gone AWOL, to whisk her off to the Chauvet-Pont-d'Arc cave in France—the location of the *Prime*—where she could finish her research in peace. The plan was another ruse, this time to draw Rainer out of hiding. Chess Team ultimately defeated Rainer, but all was nearly lost due to an unexpected threat. Sasha Therion was completely unhinged, and she had planned all along to use the knowledge gained from the Voynich and the organ to set up a harmonic in the cave that would effectively kill every living thing on Earth. Only Parker saw it coming, and he and Therion were killed by the power unleashed in that cave. While Chess Team fought off Rainer's hideously deformed army, King managed to reverse the damage of the *Prime* in the nick of time.

The events served to solidify my reasoning for the existence of Chess Team. Sometimes the threats are so great that no conventional force can handle them. And almost certainly the world would have been lost if we had needed to follow conventional channels for our covert actions. The mission also served as a poignant reminder that sometimes the greater threat is the one you don't see coming. Sasha Therion was testament to that.

Mission 01
Designate: PULSE

When the team finally came face to face with Richard Ridley, it led to death and destruction in several locations around the planet, including a volcanic eruption and the resurrection of a creature out of antiquity and mythology.

The man who would have been King's brother-in-law, George Pierce, had been called to the Nazca plains in Peru, to consult on ancient Greek writing that had been discovered by archeologist Dr. Molly McCabe. They had located the buried remains of the fabled Lernaean Hydra—a desiccated, petrified, reptilian head, which the mythical Hercules had supposedly dispatched and cauterized. Pierce asked King to come to the site to act as security for the find, but as soon as King arrived, a team of soldiers from Ridley's Gen-Y security team attacked the site, killing McCabe, trapping King in the Hydra's tomb and abducting Pierce and the remains of the creature. But before they left the site, Gen-Y injected McCabe with an experimental serum, assuring Pierce that she would somehow be fine. Sure enough, Pierce told me he watched her come back to life.

Around this time, Seth Lloyd, a programmer at Ridley's Manifold Genetics laboratory in Peru, apparently grew a conscience when he hacked the Manifold database and found out about the human regeneration experimentation in which the company had been engaged. Lloyd handed off a copy of the data to his friend, Gen-Y security agent, Anna Beck, before fleeing for his life into the jungle.

Back in Nazca, King escaped the tomb with the help of a local, only to discover that McCabe had been resurrected as a mindless creature that killed all the other expedition crew members and villagers. He tracked Gen-Y to a river and then followed them by boat, contacting me and requesting the intervention of Chess Team. I got the team in motion as King encountered human carcasses on the river, before stumbling on the remains of the Manifold facility in the jungle. Ridley had already fled with Pierce, his people and the remains of the Hydra. He had destroyed the lab, but he had left behind a surprise for King—regeneration serum-enhanced capybara. The creatures were violent and nearly indestructible, healing from most wounds. Luckily, Chess Team arrived in time to assist. At the end of the fight, the team stumbled upon Seth Lloyd's corpse and recovered a second USB flashdrive with the cracked Manifold database.

The team returned to Pope Air Force Base, and Lewis Aleman, the team's computing genius, was able to retrieve some of the data from the drive, including the location of another of Ridley's bases. His *Beta* facility was located under a volcano on Tristan Da Cunha, in the Atlantic Ocean. The man had fled there with Pierce, and along with Ridley's genetic scientist Todd Maddox, and his head of security, Oliver Reinhart, they coerced George Pierce into assisting them in their research with the Hydra's remains—up to the point of Pierce's becoming an unwilling guinea pig for a newly Hydraderived version of their regeneration/immortality serum. The results were unexpected and hideous, to say the least. George's eyes turned yellow. His skin became a thick green coating of scales; his nails became claws and his teeth transforming into fangs.

Chess Team was transported to the region via aircraft carrier and landed on the island in sub-teams—King and Queen disguised as tourists. The mission quickly went to hell, as a local resident, John Karn, first saw through King's disguise, but later became an ally and eventually a casualty. Bishop discovered a mass grave on the outskirts of the compound, just as Queen was gaining entry to the sub-volcanic facility. Bishop was captured and brought into the facility, seeing that the entire complex was rigged to be destroyed, if necessary. Rook reported that employees were evacuating as King was making his way inside. Then the base launched a volley of artillery at the aircraft carrier—the *USS Grant*—and the death toll was over five hundred.

While unsuspecting servicemen and women were dying out in the water, inside the volcanic base Queen planted a computer virus before discovering and rescuing Bishop. He revealed the urgency of the need to evacuate, but he temporarily kept something else hidden from the team—he had been injected with Ridley's pre-Hydra Regen serum, which would turn Bishop into a rage monster if he were to suffer any injury. Meanwhile, King was nearly crushed by an exiting submarine carrying Ridley to safety, on the former's way into the complex using an underwater tunnel. King then found the serpentine Pierce, who traced a symbol in blood and whispered a name before falling into a coma.

The battle outside the volcano was brief, but violent, as Ridley unleashed hundreds of locals who had been converted into Regens. The civilian, Karn, was killed, and Bishop's secret was revealed when he shielded King and Queen from flying debris with his body, as the Volcano erupted. Chess Team evacuated the area and hitched a ride on a US Navy submarine, before returning to Pope AFB.

We quickly located another Manifold research lab— *Alpha*, which was hidden under the White Mountains in New Hampshire. While Queen and Rook left for Greece to consult George Pierce's academic partner, Augustina Gallo, and to track down the mysterious symbol Pierce had drawn in blood, the rest of the team staked out the Pinckney Bible Conference campground in New Hampshire, seeking entry into the Alpha lab.

Knight gained entry to the lab, while Anna Beck, the Gen-Y security officer, having examined the contents of the drive the deceased programmer Lloyd had given to her, decided to contact King in the campground. Shortly after the cryptic meeting, King was helpless to save two children from a roaring house fire, but Bishop, heedless of the danger, rushed in and saved the children. The action should have killed him. His wounds were severe, but he healed instantly, as King watched, prepared to put a bullet in his friend, should Bishop 'turn' into one of the mindless Regens. Amazingly, Bishop managed to control the rage through sheer force of will.

In Europe, Queen, Rook, and Gallo were attacked by wraithlike creatures in Pierce's office in Athens, before locating a map of Gibraltar with the symbol of the Herculean Society. Rook and Queen escorted Gallo to safety, then made their way to Gorham's Cave, a natural sea cavern at the base of a cliff on Gibraltar. The place is the last known site of Neanderthal habitation, but as the duo would discover, it was still occupied—by the Herculean Society. Queen and Rook met a man named Alexander Diotrephes, who explained to them the purpose of the society. Existing since the times of Ancient Greece, and ostensibly dedicated to promoting the memory of Hercules, the organization actually protected the world from rare secrets of history that were better left unknown. Alexander's wraith creatures allowed Rook and Queen to pass, and the man provided them with a serum that would cure Pierce and end the Hydra. They just had to get it back to New Hampshire in time.

Stateside, King and Bishop followed Knight's GPS signal, entering the Alpha facility, as Knight—with some assistance from Anna Beck—located the Hydra head. Unfortunately, a gunfight broke out shortly after Beck slipped away, and the head was splashed with liquid during the battle.

And it began to grow...

Beck took out the security surveillance team and returned just in time to help Knight extricate himself from the Hydra's clutches. It had already regrown three heads and killed several Gen-Y men. Knight and Beck met up with Bishop and King, and the four retreated from the lab as Ridley gave the general evacuation order on this complex, too. The group exited to the campground, doing their best to protect the well meaning Manifold scientists, but the Hydra attacked several of them, and partially ate many. And the creature was still growing.

While Rook and Queen flew back to the U.S. in *Crescent*, Bishop went toe to toe with the Hydra a few times, sustaining heavy injuries, but regenerating as quickly from his wounds as the creature did. With seven heads at this point and nearly the size of a Mack truck, the beast was putting up quite a fight. The Hydra killed several Manifold scientists and Gen-Y officers along the way, as it steadily headed toward the populated area of the campground and the innocent civilians who were oblivious to the oncoming danger. Ridley's head geneticist, Todd Maddox, was among the casualties, but he managed to warn Chess Team of Ridley's destruct mechanism in the Alpha facility—the entire complex sat over a cave filled with natural gas. The device's explosion itself would pale in comparison to the compounded effects.

King and Beck chased after Ridley and his chief of security, Reinhart, while Knight crashed a Humvee into the Hydra, severely injuring it. But the creature's regenerative traits brought it rapidly back into the fight. Only Bishop could keep the thing at bay. But the toll on him could have been catastrophic. King and Beck dispatched Reinhart, and from the air in a helicopter, King secured Ridley's handheld digital device in a fistfight. The device could shut down the destruction mechanism in the base. Ridley, though, had taken his own serum, and no longer fearing death, the madman leapt from the helicopter to his apparent demise.

As Knight and Bishop were about to be overwhelmed by the Hydra, King came to the rescue with the helicopter's rotary canon, and then Rook and Queen arrived. Halo-jumping from *Crescent*, Queen injected the Hydra with the cure Alexander had provided, while Rook blasted the creature with an anti-tank rocket, for the perfect one-two punch. The fight with the creature over, one more battle remained: Rook had to talk Bishop down from the Regen rage that was coursing through his body. He succeeded, and Lewis Aleman halted the doomsday countdown, while Anna Beck slipped away.

We covered up the incident at the campground, with US Army hazmat teams coming in to sweep the camp and the captured base. Ridley's body was gone, and we surmised that his experiments had indeed brought him back to life. We knew we would encounter him again, but we had no way of knowing what an impact he would have on our lives. Pierce was cured, although the remedy Alexander had provided the team was useless on Bishop. When Chess Team, along with Pierce, returned to Gibraltar, they found that Alexander, his archeologists and his protective wraiths had all cleared out, leaving only the Herculean Society symbol behind as a warning for the team to not pursue them. George posited that Alexander was actually the legendary Hercules. Although the team had been warned not to follow him, he resurfaced in our lives again, too. He, like Ridley, would have a lasting impact on the team, and especially on King.

Mission 02
Designate: INSTINCT

In 2010, the President of the United States dropped dead of an unusual strain of the Brugada—or Sudden Death—virus, which had been tailored to piggy-back on an avian influenza. The Secret Service were able to revive him, and Chess Team were quickly mobilized. They would take CDC scientist Dr. Sara Fogg to the interior of Vietnam, searching for the source of the virus, and the cure. Each member of the team was surgically fitted with a cardioverter defibrilator to bring them back from the dead, should they succumb to the disease while out in the field.

Unfortunately the team parachuted into a hot landing zone, as members of the Vietnamese army were engaged with a rogue element of the Khmer Rouge, and the whole group of combatants were pursued by...something else. Chess Team, with Fogg now acting under the temporary callsign of Pawn, rendezvoused with Sommalina Syha, a local intelligence asset designated Pawn Two. The group was pursued by the winners of the scuffle at the LZ—the Vietnam People's Liberation Army *Death Volunteers*, a fanatical group of Vietnamese special forces.

As Pawn took a sample of blood from an old villager who survived an outbreak of Brugada, and who might have possessed a natural cure, Rook died and the cardioverter defibrilator brought him back. Using old Vietcong tunnels, the VPLA pressed the attack. Pawn Two had been informing for the VPLA, because of a debt her father owed their leader, Major General Nguyen Trung. They betrayed her and tried to kill her. Fogg was abducted, and King and Queen pursed the VPLA in the tunnels. Meanwhile Knight was fighting against the ferocious creatures that were pursuing the VPLA in the jungle. Rook, Bishop and Pawn Two were forced into the tunnels.

Back in Washington, the White House was under a secret quarantine as Secret Service searched for all those infected between patient zero and the President. Domenick Boucher and I watched via satellite as Chess Team appeared to be buried under a landslide in Vietnam. Then the inevitable happened: the press got word of the Brugada epidemic.

Rook, Bishop and Pawn Two were startled in the tunnels when a creature, later revealed to be a devolved Neanderthal/Human Hybrid, dumped Knight near their location. At the same time, King and Queen tracked Pawn down to a small village controlled by the VPLA, but it was a trap and they were captured and tortured by Trung. The vicious general branded the VPLA Death Volunteer symbol into Queen's forehead before fleeing in terror from her ability to withstand pain and the implied threat of her revenge. Pawn freed King and Queen, and the three fled the camp as the remnants of the Khmer attacked. Queen returned to the village seeking revenge on Trung, killing eleven men before she was forced to retreat. She did, however, retrieve Pawn's backpack and the blood sample that most likely had the cure. Pawn Two made up for her betrayal by sacrificing herself to save Bishop and Rook, and Knight went deeper into the mountain to lay low, as he was in no shape to fight.

Rook and Bishop encountered Dr. Anthony Weston, a cryptozoologist who had disappeared in Vietnam in 1995. The man had encountered the Nguoi Rung, a race of devolved Neanderthals that had survived the ages in the interior of the densely jungle-covered country. Their males had died out, and the 'Old Mothers' had forcibly mated with Weston, creating a new race of Hybrids, who aged to full adult in just a few short years. With Weston as the Alpha, the new race had grown to nearly 2000 strong. Weston and one of his Hybrids seemingly killed Bishop before later capturing King and Sara Fogg. On his own, and furious at the perceived loss of his teammate, Rook met up with Queen and they planned to infiltrate the mountain dwelling of Weston's brood.

Inside the mountain, Knight found Weston's original journal, detailing his academic findings on the Neanderthals, as well as a series of strange crystal formations. Weston admitted to King and Fogg that he knew of the virus killing humanity, but he was more concerned with the survival of his offspring. He planned to use Fogg as a teacher for the Hybrids and left King to be eaten by his favorite great-great-granddaughter. King out-thought the Hybrid, and Fogg discovered Weston was immune to the Brugada as a result of a sexually transmitted disease from the Old Mothers—the devolved Neanderthals. Thinking on her feet, Fogg attacked Weston and allowed him to strike her, splitting her lip. She bit him, their blood mingling, and the cure passing to her, before she escaped.

In another part of the subterranean city, Knight was attacked by a mindless Regen Bishop, whose altered DNA from the Hydra affair had saved his life, but cost him his mind. Luckily, the strange crystals in the cavern had an amazing restorative effect on everyone—including Bishop, and they kept his mind intact. Taking a piece of the crystal with him, he and Knight sought out the others. Meanwhile, King succumbed to the Brugada, and because his implanted CD device had been shorted out as a result of Trung's torture, Fogg needed to bring him back manually.

Outside, Trung and his men penetrated the mountain, bypassing Weston and his Hybrids by once again resorting to ancient VC tunnels. Queen and Rook were separated in the mountain, when Red, the largest and most aggressive Old Mother, abducted Rook to be her new mate. Queen later found King and Pawn, while Rook convinced Red and the Old Mothers to kill Weston, agreeing that he would only become their mate if they did his bidding.

Chess Team was reunited, and King set explosives to destroy the compound. Fogg passed the cure to King and Queen via a blood exchange, and the team made their escape as the VPLA did battle with the Hybrids. But first Queen killed Trung with a single head-butt, which set off the chaos.

The mountain was destroyed, the VPLA were easily dispatched by the Hybrids and Chess Team fled down river, pursued by Weston, the Hybrids and the Old Mothers, who were intent on mating with Rook. King managed to kill Weston, and most of the Hybrids and Neanderthals were killed by superior firepower, when, as Deep Blue, I arrived with a platoon of Delta operators. Rook intervened in the killing of Red and the last remaining Hybrids, letting them live in peace, before the team was whisked away ahead of the arrival of conventional Vietnamese forces.

At the end of this mission, I revealed my identity to the team, and they were shocked to learn the President of the United States was secretly Deep Blue, but they finally understood why—between Presidential duties and the quarantine—I had not been able to assist them on the bulk of the mission. The cure was disseminated, and two more good things came at the end of the mission. King and Sara Fogg found comfort and happiness in each other, and six weeks later King traveled to the Siletz reservation in Oregon, sent by his friend George Pierce. The town had been destroyed along with all its inhabitants, but a young girl of eleven was alive, and had been left behind for King to discover, by the legendary Hercules. In time, she would become King's adopted daughter...but first she would set into motion a dire series of events.

Mission 03
Designate: THRESHOLD

Six months after the massacre in Siletz, Oregon, King was formally granted custody of Fiona Apserkahar Lane. While Utah senator Lance Marrs began a rich smear campaign against the Duncan administration, other wheels were set in motion. The following year, King learned of his mother's death. While at the burial, he met his father—Peter Sigler—a man who had abandoned the family many years earlier. Peter revealed that Lynn Sigler's death was all for show. It turned out that Peter and Lynn Sigler had been Russian spies earlier in life, but they had defected to the West. Peter claimed to have spent ten years in a US prison (which later turned out to be a lie), and now Russia was trying to reactivate them as assets, so they had faked Lynn's death—or so their story went.

While King was dealing with personal business, Chess Team received word from Alexander Diotrephes that King was needed to help safeguard the last speakers of several dying languages around the world, because someone was hunting and exterminating them. The team deployed back to Vietnam and to Australia, only to meet opposition and failure on both missions. But their opponents were unexpected to say the least—massive stone and crystal golems. They destroyed what may have been the last of the Hybrids and devolved Neanderthals at Mount Meru in Vietnam before Rook and Queen could stop the creatures, and the aboriginals in Australia were slaughtered before Bishop and Knight could intervene.

At the same time, Fort Bragg was attacked by a stone golem resembling a giant rhino. Fiona, who was being watched by Lewis Aleman at the time, was clearly the target. Dozens were killed or injured before Alexander appeared at the last minute and whisked Fiona off to safety. King and the Siglers arrived at the end of the battle to discover that Fiona was gone.

Additional Delta operators were appended to Chess Team so the five key operators could split up around the globe, racing to find the world's endangered language speakers before the hideous rock creatures could obliterate them. Bishop and Queen led separate teams to South America, while Knight led a team to Taiwan and Rook took a team to Siberia. King and George Pierce made their way to Rome, hunting Alexander and Fiona. The latter, as a Type 1 diabetic, had just three days of insulin from her pump.

Aside from King and Pierce finding Alexander under the ruins of the Roman Forum, all the other missions were a bust. Richard Ridley, the man behind the golems, had informed each of the foreign governments of the impending Delta missions on their respective sovereign soils. Each mission went poorly, with Knight losing most of his team, and Rook losing all of his. Ridley's golems attacked Alexander's lair—the tomb of his wife Acca Larentia. Fiona was captured, and Alexander and King, with the help of Alexander's wraiths and Pierce, managed to escape the fury of Ridley's creatures. Alexander and King next headed to Israel, to consult an expert on golems—a man who was both a rabbi and a physicist. Bishop, Knight and Queen were recalled and sent to Guatemala, after Ridley was sighted there. Unfortunately, the man had also been spotted in England—at the exact same time!

We soon realized Ridley had control over the Mother Tongue, an ancient protolanguage believed to be the language of humanity prior to the Tower of Babel story—the actual language of God. He was now capable of granting life to inanimate objects like stone. He also appeared to be able to duplicate himself from clay and alter the DNA of other living things. King and Alexander were attacked by giant, mutated sandfish skinks before racing to Stonehenge to confront the second Ridley. They found a body that was most likely that of Merlin, before dealing with tunnel collapses and yet more golems, while needing to protect civilians. The others encountered a Ridley duplicate under a Mayan step pyramid called La Danta. Bishop saved the others yet again, by using his Regen abilities—the negative side effects of which were kept in check by the crystal from Mount Meru, which he wore around his neck like a talisman.

In Washington, Boucher and I set in motion the inevitable plan I had for departing the presidency, should my work with the team become too demanding. It dovetailed nicely with Senator Marrs's dogged political attacks. In Guatemala, after battling a sea of animated skeletons with his team, Knight killed the Ridley duplicate, which returned to clay. At Stonehenge, King and Alexander briefly dealt with the stones of the monument themselves transforming into a golem, before the structure collapsed—no longer animated.

On his own in Russia, injured and dejected, Rook found shelter with an old woman, who quickly became a casualty of Rook's escape from Russian forces—but not before she sent Rook to her brother, Maksim Dashkov, in Severodvinsk, on the White Sea. Dashkov agreed to take Rook out of Russia on his fishing vessel. However, he wasn't the only passenger on that voyage.

King and Alexander returned to Israel to once again meet with the rabbi, but when Alexander tried to take control of the situation, the rest of Chess Team arrived and King made it clear that Alexander was working for him—and not the other way around. King also discovered that Ridley had been tracking him, when he found that his parents had slipped an electronic bug into his clothes. The group soon realized Ridley's intent to broadcast the Mother Tongue, remaking the world as he saw fit. Lewis Aleman found traces of soil from the US Camp Alpha in one of the golem creatures, and the team raced for Iraq, searching for Ridley and the Tower of Babel.

Under the sands of the desert, King discovered the Hanging Gardens of Babylon instead of the Tower, but Ridley had been there first, and he had left a deadly trap behind, with more mutant golem sandfish and giant desert mantises. As the team battled those creatures, Fiona, as Ridley's captive, who was at the real Tower location—under Pontus, Turkey, began to overhear and memorize several utterances of the Mother Tongue.

Chess Team soon made for Turkey and entered the ruins. They discovered Ridley's control of the Mother Tongue had extended to creating light when they came across floating miniature suns. He had also used his powers to heal Fiona of her dehydration and to brainwash her into fooling Knight and Bishop, and attacking King with a knife. Ridley himself was still afflicted with a hideous side effect of his first attempt with the Mother Tongue—a newly conjoined duplicate Ridley growing from the original's back. As chaos erupted, the team battling golems and other mutated animals on all fronts, Bishop disposed of his crystal and went full-on Regen to attack Ridley. Ridley surprised everyone by countering the attack with curing Bishop of his affliction, but removing his miraculous ability to heal in the process.

Fiona was freed from Ridley's thrall and King, amped up on an adrenaline-boosting serum of Alexander's, stopped the broadcast, killed the conjoined duplicate and beheaded the true Richard Ridley. Alexander got King to safety, following the others as they retreated from the collapsing subterranean structure. The mountain imploded, and Fiona used the Mother Tongue to stop the last of the golems, before passing out.

On his way to Norway, Rook dealt with some Russian gangsters aboard Dashkov's boat, freeing their captive, one Asya Machtcenko, a woman who would play a much larger role in the lives of every Chess Team member. In America, King was cured of his massive traumatic injuries by George Pierce, who had swiped some of the famed Appleseeds of Hesperides from Alexander's base in Rome. The Siglers had flown the coop, the President resigned, seemingly in disgrace, and Vice President Chambers was sworn in. And although we would not discover it for some time, Richard Ridley had survived even his beheading—but his new situation was far worse than death.

Mission 03.1
Designate: CALLSIGN: KING

After the horrors Richard Ridley had perpetrated on the team, Rook was AWOL, and Queen was released to search for him. As the other team members left for their respective vacations, a Nexus Genetic Research expedition in Ethiopia was going horribly wrong. In a cavern at the site, most of the researchers became mindless drones—as if their abilities for higher reasoning had simply been switched off. One of the camp laborers, Moses Selassie, fled the site, bringing one of the scientists, American Dr. Felice Carter, to a hospital in Addis Ababa.

We might not have known, if King's girlfriend, epidemiologist Sara Fogg had not been called to the capital to consult on Dr. Carter's case. As King went there to meet up with her, his taxi was assaulted by mercenaries. After quickly dispatching them, King raced to the hospital where another team was slaughtering Dr. Fogg's team. Before King could get to her, Fogg (along with a sample of Carter's blood) was swept to safety by Max Fulbright, a man claiming to be an embassy attaché. Instead of Fogg, King found Felice Carter, who had woken up.

Together with Carter and Moses Selassie, King returned to the Nexus site. It turned out that Nexus was a subsidiary of Manifold Genetics. King and the others discovered the fabled elephant graveyard in the cavern at the Nexus site, and the scientists that had been left behind were still functioning, but mindlessly. Upon arrival, Carter also appeared to lose her mind.

Meanwhile, Fulbright took Dr. Fogg on an assault of a floating Manifold bioweapons development facility off the coast of Somalia, where the scientists there had apparently already begun weaponizing the virus that had been discovered at the elephant graveyard. The facility was destroyed, and Fulbright and Fogg headed for the expedition site to retrieve the source DNA.

At the site, Felice Carter awoke and realized that she was responsible for switching off the minds of her fellow scientists. Believing herself possessed by the 'Old Mother,' an evil spirit thousands of years old, she realized she had the ability to control other humans—in some cases involuntarily. Moses Selassie betrayed King and Carter, seeking to control the wealth of the ivory in the cavern, ensuring an Africa for Africans. He brought in rebel soldiers, and King fought them off aided by the zombie-like scientists that rallied to protect Carter.

Fogg and Fulbright then arrived, with Fulbright revealing his true allegiance to a worldwide artificial-intelligence computer network called Brainstorm, with ties deep into the military-industrial complex. He drugged and abducted Carter, killed Selassie and left his mercenaries to kill King. King managed to escape with the help of the mindless scientists, and he hijacked a helicopter, chasing Fulbright's own helicopter down. Unfortunately, Fulbright had Brainstorm call in the Ethiopian Air Force, which shot down King's helicopter. Plunging only sixty feet, King survived the crash, but he led Fulbright into thinking he was dead.

After *Crescent* picked King up, he made his way to Algeria, the home of Graham Brown, who posed as

Brainstorm's assistant. Brown was in fact an inveterate gambler with a phenomenal mind for probability, who had carefully constructed the Brainstorm persona. Working under duress for him, Fogg hypothesized that the human race had been exposed to a particular retrovirus that had been the pivotal event in the evolution of human consciousness. Carter was quantum entangled with the whole of humanity, and she had involuntarily turned off the genome responsible for human sentience.

King arrived in Algeria, and fought Fulbright, before Carter simply switched the man off. Brown escaped, but not before calling in a cruise missile on the house. Fogg believed that should Carter be killed, she might accidentally switch off the whole human race with her evolutionary regression powers. King, Fogg and Carter escaped the house just in time. King later returned to the elephant graveyard and at Fogg's behest destroyed the site, so the virus it contained could not infect anyone else. Carter was treated for post-traumatic stress disorder and learned to keep her ability in check. But we had not heard the last from Brainstorm.

Mission 03.2
Designate: CALLSIGN: QUEEN

While King was in Ethiopia, Queen was beginning her search for Rook when Endgame diverted her to Pripyat, the town near the infamous Soviet nuclear meltdown at Chernobyl. After seizing one of Richard Ridley's bases, we had learned from his data files of other labs and projects. The one in the Ukraine was of such importance that we sent Queen in immediately.

She quickly found that a group of teenaged urban explorers had been on site and were attacked by something resembling a werewolf. Queen also did brief battle with one of the 'Oborots' before attempting to whisk a teenage girl to safety. The town's dilapidated amusement park was the locus of Oborot activity, and Queen suspected the Manifold lab was below it. Suddenly Manifold security agents were assaulting her.

Dispatching the men sent after her, Queen found that they had killed the young girl under her protection. Vowing revenge, she infiltrated the amusement park, only to discover that it was filled with death traps. Then the lab intentionally released a horde of Oborots to hunt Queen down. She managed to evade the traps and the creatures, following an injured Oborot down its secret entrance into the lab.

Queen quickly found a scientist to interrogate and learned of the human experimentation that had been going on at the lab. She also learned that the man running the facility, who we later discovered was Richard Ridley's brother Darius, was going to release all the failed test subjects—horribly malformed Oborot creatures, most of whom were criminals or volunteers. Manifold's failed super soldiers rampaged through the facility while Queen did battle with Darius, chewing one of his ears off in the fight.

Queen was eventually forced to flee the burning lab with dozens of Oborots chasing her. She ascended the Fujiyama building—the tallest in town. She leapt off the roof, wingsuit-gliding to safety, while the horde of Oborots either leapt after her to their deaths or were destroyed by the grenades she left behind on the roof.

A local contact was waiting for her at the river. To Queen's surprise, when the man spied a photograph she had of Rook, he claimed to have seen Rook in Severodvinsk, boarding Maksim Dashkov's ship the *Songbird*. With a solid lead to follow, Queen abandoned Siberia in favor of Severodvinsk. And of course, we had not seen the last of Darius Ridley.

Mission 03.3
Designate: CALLSIGN: ROOK

While Queen was searching for Rook and battling muscular, hairy creatures, Rook was getting his own taste of the wolf in Norway. Needing time away after the slaughter of his team in Siberia, Rook had traveled with Maksim Dashkov to Norway. Parting ways with the rescued Asya Machtcenko, he wandered into the small town of Fenris Kystby. His stay was anything but peaceful, but ultimately, his presence there saved the world.

Rook met a farmer named Peder Bjork, who allowed Rook to sleep in his barn in exchange for tracking down whatever was killing the man's livestock. Because the town had no phones, Rook was unable to call in to Endgame HQ. He took the deal and soon discovered how peculiarly xenophobic the town was. Peder took Rook into town to get some food at the general store, where Rook found that the inhabitants of the small village also did not use currency. Rook next met Eirek Fossen, the unofficial mayor of the town, who attempted to persuade Rook to leave. Fossen assured Rook and Peder that a roaming pack of wolves Rook had seen upon entering the town were protecting the livestock—something else was attacking Peder's cows. Something the locals called 'Ulverja.' The creature was said to be nine feet tall, with long legs and a hairy body. In other words, it was a sort of Scandinavian Bigfoot.

Rook stalked the creature over a few nights. Before reaching success with his endeavors, a man came to the barn late one night and tried to kill Rook. It turned out to be Jens Fossen—Eirek Fossen's son. Rook and Peder dispatched the body and upped their security awareness as Fossen Sr. agreed to help Rook in his hunt for Ulverja, apologizing for his initial hostility. Fossen was apparently a research scientist working with wolves, hence the protective pack that was roaming the area. After another clash with the Ulverja, and a hint from a local to pay attention to the creature's victims, Rook discovered its lair in an abandoned Nazi *Ahnenerbe* research lab, buried under a hillside.

After yet another attempt on his life, Rook enlisted Fossen—who believed the creature had killed his son—in laying a trap for the Ulverja in the lab. Rook found and pocketed an envelope in the facility before he and Fossen did quick battle with the creature, mortally wounding it.

The creature was revealed to be Edmund Kiss—a former Nazi scientist who had experimented with wolves before Fossen. Kiss was actually Fossen's father, and the note he left in the envelope implored Fossen to seal a gateway, mentioning something about 'Dire Wolves.'

We would later discover that Eirek Fossen was involved in the whole affair much deeper. The world would meet the Dire Wolves to its peril, and we were all lucky that Rook decided to stay in town and dig a little deeper into the mysteries of Fenris Kystby.

Mission 03.4
Designate: CALLSIGN: KING – UNDERWORLD

Around the time King was accompanying his friend
George Pierce, in visiting the latter's addict brother,
something attacked US Highway 60 between Mesa and
Globe, in Arizona. Police arriving on site found no
bodies but did find a video that was disturbing enough
to call in the National Guard.

Lewis Aleman called to ask King to investigate the
Bigfoot-like shaggy creatures known as the Mogollon
Monsters, and because one of them in the video the
police officer found was wearing an ancient Greek
medallion, King shanghaied Pierce into the mission. But
unbeknownst to King, Brainstorm, still smarting over
his defeat in Algeria, had hired retired master assassin,
Ivan Sokoloff, to kill him. Sokoloff and his support team
failed to kill King or Pierce, though, and the latter two
made their way to the Sonoran Desert.

They arrived in time to save paranormal investigator Nina Raglan from a rattlesnake, and in time to
be arrested by soldiers who had cordoned off the
area near the Mogollon Monster attacks. Before the
soldiers could remove them from the area, a fog
rapidly set in and the creatures returned, tearing the
base apart. When the fog had cleared, George Pierce
was gone.

Pierce had run and fallen into a cave system, and
was protected by a soldier named De Bord. They
discovered that the furry covering of the creatures was
actually a cloak, and underneath the fabric they were

maroon, lumpy humanoid things. Before Pierce and De Bord could escape, the tunnel sealed them in.

King and Raglan escaped the destroyed base and found another nearby, also ransacked. Contact with Aleman revealed that the copper mine in the area was leased to BlueLight Technologies, an energy company with lucrative DARPA contracts. King infiltrated a lab at the mine, only to discover that BlueLight's founder, Aaron Copeland, was working with Brainstorm on a DARPA project. The project was causing ball lightning and attracting the Mogollon Monsters.

Pierce and De Bord escaped the cavern system after Pierce hypothesized that it was a global system, based on observing the creatures and the coins they coveted. Pierce and De Bord got separated, and once outside and with reception again, Pierce called King for a pickup. De Bord—actually Sokoloff the assassin—killed several soldiers, and still hunted King. But he was too late. Soldiers captured King, Pierce and Raglan, bringing them before Copeland, back at the mine. Copeland revealed that the BlueLight technology was bombarding matter with antimatter, and harvesting the resulting energy, but that the system had to be shut down after just eight minutes. If not, the process could ignite the planet's atmosphere. King tried to persuade Copeland to abandon the project, which was attracting the Mogollon Monsters, but the man refused.

When the system was next activated, a massive horde of the creatures attacked the facility and engaged the defending soldiers. When Copeland had second thoughts, Sokoloff arrived and killed him at Brainstorm's behest. Pierce and Raglan retreated as the Mogollon Monsters overran the facility.

Outside, King spotted a transformer station that might have stopped the out-of-control BlueLight process. He drove a humvee off a cliff at the transformer station, disrupting power to the runaway technology, and shutting the atmospheric reaction down in the nick of time. The BlueLight station imploded just as King was attacked by a desperate Sokoloff. The fight was brutal, but King prevailed. Then he followed his instincts, texting Brainstorm from Sokoloff's phone that the contract had been fulfilled, claiming, as Sokoloff, that he had killed King. It was just the beginning of a plan King was putting together to find and eliminate Graham Brown and his Brainstorm alter ego.

Mission 03.5
Designate: CALLSIGN: BISHOP

In Iran, two villagers, fleeing jihadists stumbled across an abandoned Manifold bioweapons lab in the desert. One of them unwittingly drank a bottle of a fungus compound, Ergot-B, thinking it was drinking water. He killed his companion, and the jihadists chasing them found the lab and seized the stash of the deadly substance. Eli Jacobs, the man who was tasked with cleanup of the Manifold Alpha facility in New Hampshire, so that Chess Team could begin to use the base for the newly expanded Endgame organization, discovered notes on the substance and the lab in the old Manifold mainframe.

We quickly dispatched Erik Somers, the former Bishop, to Iran. As it turned out, he had recently been contacted by another Delta operator in country, informing him that the man—callsign: Joker—had discovered evidence of Bishop's true parentage. Temporarily sidelining meeting with his birth parents, Bishop, an American of Iranian descent who had been adopted by Midwestern parents, traveled with Joker to the old Manifold lab.

Upon arrival in country, Bishop quickly noticed that he was being followed. Joker lost the tail, and also informed Bishop of the bad news—his father, Dawoud Abbasi, was a terrorist. The man was a top recruiter for multiple terror groups, but to his relief, Bishop learned that his mother, Faiza, was completely innocent of her husband's business dealings.

Joker flew Bishop in a Cessna out to the lab, near the village of Hassi in the Kavir Desert. They met with an ally of Joker's, an ex-Iranian special forces man named Ilias. The men then journeyed on ATVs to the buried laboratory. After narrowly evading a booby trap left behind by the jihadists, they found the lab had been looted, although Bishop obtained a discarded bottle of the Ergot compound and the hidden security discs containing video footage—they hoped—of the break in. But upon exiting the lab, they found themselves seemingly under attack.

A helicopter arrived and Ilias opened fire on it, starting a gunfight that resulted in Ilias's death and the helicopter crashing. Joker claimed the discs with the security footage had been damaged, and Bishop and Joker fled before the men in the helicopter—Iranian special forces, and the men that were supposed to be Bishop's contacts in country—found Joker's discarded and still fully intact backpack, with the security camera footage.

Joker was secretly working for Dawoud Abbasi and had been sent to bring Bishop to his father. He drugged Bishop and brought him to Abbasi's base of operations in the *Naqsh-e-Rustam* ruins, the burial site of Xerxes I. Abbasi was in for a surprise, though. Upon seeing Bishop, he quickly realized that his wife had been unfaithful to him. Bishop did not resemble Abbasi at all, but he clearly resembled Anwar Muaddah, Abbasi's driver.

Abbasi killed Joker in a rage, and then dragged Faiza and Muaddah in front of Bishop, preparing to kill the father and son in front of his anguished wife. Abbasi shot Muaddah, before Bishop, with the help of Faiza, managed to break free. He stopped Abbasi just before the Iranian special forces arrived—but not before a brief skirmish with Abbasi's men, some of whom were inadvertently infected with the Ergot-B and turned into rampaging madmen.

The battle was brief, but violent, and after discovering that Faiza had been informing on him in the hopes of emigrating to the US, and with nothing left to lose, Dawoud Abbasi broke free and voluntarily ingested more of the Ergot compound. After another short battle, Bishop killed the man.

The remains of the deadly compound were collected and destroyed, and Iranian forces managed to shut down a few terror branches with the information gained in the raid. On a personal note, Erik Somers was happily reunited with his birth mother, and they formed a decent relationship, with the former helping the latter relocate to the United States. It was a well deserved, but short lived happiness for the warrior known as Bishop.

Mission 03.6
Designate: CALLSIGN: KNIGHT

To say that we were a long time dealing with the clean up of Richard Ridley's megalomaniacal dabblings in genetic research would be a massive understatement on a par with calling the Sun a warm vacation spot. While King was embroiled with Brainstorm, and the others were dealing with their various personal issues, Shin Dae-jung, callsign: Knight, was just trying to have a nice vacation in Thailand when he was recalled and sent—still wearing nightclubbing clothes—to a Chinese ghost city in the middle of the country. The Chinese had long subscribed to a 'build it and they will come' philosophy, but many of the cities they've constructed in the interior of China are still mostly vacant. Shenhuang was one such place—but for a few former Manifold scientists at a Chinese genetic research station, run by an out-of-control addict, Phillip Cho. They had secured a sample of the Hydra's DNA from scientists that had fled the Alpha lab in New Hampshire, and they were attempting to create a weapon for the Chinese Motherland.

Knight never got a briefing, nor did he reach his rendezvous with British commandos. His transport plane was knocked out of the sky by an electromagnetic pulse, and he and the pilot crash-landed on an abandoned parking structure, before quickly being hunted by a monstrosity resembling the Hydra, which Knight had faced once before.

Knight rescued the children of one of the maintenance workers and shepherded them to safety before running into Anna Beck, the former Pawn who had helped with Chess Team's infiltration of the Alpha lab in New Hampshire. She had been working with the British and tracking down and destroying old Manifold projects. The two evaded the creature, Huangdi, by hitting it with a 5000 pound Humvee, but they discovered the genetic monstrosity possessed the regenerative abilities of the original Hydra.

While this was happening, Philip Cho, half mad with power and the other half paranoid on cocaine, imprisoned his research partner, the former Manifold scientist Giuseppi Salvatori. Still possessing a conscience, Salvatori escaped from Cho's clutches and set a self destruct mechanism that would wipe out the city—and the hideous nine-foot-tall, part human, part Hydra abomination that was Huangdi.

Knight and Beck finally met up with the remains of the British commando unit, and they collectively battled and fled from Huangdi, before coming up with a tentative plan to use a thermobaric bomb on the downed Osprey that had transported Knight to China. Nabbing a car battery from outside the range of the EMP burst that had downed the plane, Knight and the others were able to rig the bomb to be detonated as a standalone device—but it required the injured SAS Commander, William Donahue, to stay behind to trigger it. Knight temporarily distracted the creature by covering it in jet fuel and igniting it—the creature's regenerative abilities barely keeping up with the continual combustion. Unfortunately, Huangdi made it to a body of water, dousing itself before once more taking up the chase.

Cho, in a fit of madness and despair at his failings with the regenerative serum, and no longer in command of his senses because of the drugs, injured Salvatori before ingesting his latest—and according to Salvatori, unperfected—variant of the serum. He changed into a massive, 40-foot-tall cross between the Hydra, a burn patient and the elephant man.

Donahue detonated the bomb, killing Huangdi, but Knight and Beck still had the kaiju-sized version of Cho on their heels. Beck retrieved the children and Salvatori, learning of the self-destruct mechanism that would wipe out both the city and the Hydra-infected Cho-thing. As she hustled them all to a waiting helicopter, the Cho creature chased Knight down, nearly killing him when it picked up and threw a mini-van Knight had been driving—with him still in it.

Surviving the resulting crash, Knight dropped a construction crane on the Cho-thing, impaling it with an I-beam, and delaying it long enough for Beck to rescue Knight and get them all to safety. The self destruct was a nuclear-level event, and it wiped out the city, and we assume, Cho. Knight and Beck began a relationship shortly after the event, and she accepted an offer to become Endgame's chief of internal security, which she excelled at. She would prove her worth at the Endgame headquarters, when her endurance was put to the test.

Mission 03.7
Designate: CALLSIGN: DEEP BLUE

While the members of Chess Team were each experiencing craziness around the world, I set about updating our newly acquired headquarters—the captured Manifold Genetics *Alpha* laboratory under the White Mountains of New Hampshire. As one of my final acts as President, I had arranged a cleanup of the facility with US Army resources. After I had stepped down, it was time to take Chess Team away from the military, and time for me to assume the mantle of Deep Blue full time. But the transition was anything but easy—I was almost eaten before I had the chance.

On a routine inspection of the new base, I was trapped inside of it, when an invading team of Manifold's former security forces, Gen-Y, led by Irish mercenary Martin Damien, penetrated the base and seized control of the computer systems. All security doors were shut, and booby traps the Army had missed were activated. My own newly hired Endgame security force, led by Matt Carrack, callsign: White One, was trapped outside the base, while Lori Stanton, my right hand assistant, and I attempted to stop Damien's men.

Carrack's men were all killed attempting to gain access to the base, and Anna Beck, who on my orders was exploring the giant, natural gas-filled cavern under the *Labs* section of the base, found out the hard way that there was yet another threat waiting for us in the darkness.

Damien's forces had apparently returned to the base to secure a sample of something so twisted, even

Richard Ridley had not considered it. Ridley's lead researcher, Todd Maddox, had experimented with Ridley's Regen serum on some native New Hampshire salamanders. The little beasties also received proteins from the Hydra and other creatures, before they were unknowingly exposed to massive quantities of the region's subterranean uranium deposits. If that wasn't enough, the creatures were stored in cages below the lab where Knight's battle with Gen-Y in 2009 splashed chemicals all over the inert Hydra, bringing it fully back to life. Unnoticed in the resulting chaos, the chemical soup drained into the lower level, coating the salamanders, which became aggressive, and broke free from their constraints. The creatures delved into the deepest corners of the underground base, reproducing and waiting for a new food source. Damien's men, in hoping to acquire one of the salamander eggs, provided that spark, and sent Beck and I running for our lives.

Carrack eventually breached the base, but only after losing all of his men. One of the amped-up salamanders killed Lori Stanton. To her credit, she regained computer control of the base before her horrible death. I sent Beck and Carrack to the *Labs* portion of the facility to stop the self-destruct device Damien had brought, while I chased his men into the *Dock* section of the base, hoping to stop them, and evading hordes of killer salamanders along the way. One bright spot was that the creatures shied from light and feared fire. Armed with rockets and an antique flamethrower, I entered the *Dock* only to find that Damien's men had made a mess of things.

While Damien slipped back to the *Central* portion of the base via the light-rail trains that connected the sprawling subterranean complex, I fought off the remains of his men and the thrashing, regenerating salamanders. Once I realized he was after the eggs, I knew I had to shut Damien down before he opened the outer door from the *Dock*, which had allowed Ridley access to the sea via a massively long submerged tunnel. It facilitated his Russian Typhoon submarine—now *my* submarine—in getting to open water some sixty miles away on the small New Hampshire coastline. Unfortunately, I never got to use the sub before discovering what had taken up residence in it.

The salamanders were protecting a giant matriarch that had gotten into and made a lair in the sub's cargo space, which had been converted into a mini-sub moon-pool and dock. With a thirty-foot-wide head, the thing had grown so large it couldn't get out of the sub any longer. I fired a rocket at the thing in the dark, escaping the conflagration just in time.

Back in the *Labs*, Carrack and Beck parachuted into the deep cavern under the base, and retrieved the bomb. They were unable to defuse it, but they moved it higher into the base, and far from the deposits of natural gas, dumping it in a chemical safe and running for cover before the explosion. A significant part of the *Labs* section of the base was damaged, but their quick thinking and even quicker reflexes stopped the destruction of a larger part of new Hampshire and saved countless civilian lives.

The problem in *Dock* dealt with, I tracked Damien down to the vehicle hangar in the *Central* section of the base. Unknown to me at the time, Carrack had arranged with General Keasling for an Abrams tank to come up to the base, to assist in breaching the huge steel hangar door. As soldiers were outside the hangar, preparing to shoot their way in with the 120mm big gun, I was engaged in a vicious knife fight with Damien in the dark of the hangar, before I slipped away into the dark and climbed into one of our parked MH-60 Black Hawk helicopters. When he stepped in front of the missiles, I turned on the floodlights and launched a Hellfire missile at Damien, killing him and blasting the huge hangar door right out of the cliff wall, flinging it on top of a very surprised Abrams tank crew, who thankfully were protected by the vehicle's composite armor.

It took a while to round up the remaining salamanders and their eggs, and to scour every nook and cranny of the extensive base, assuring ourselves there were no more surprises waiting for us. We refitted the security systems, and I upgraded the complement of security personnel, promoting Carrack to the role of White Zero, head of security, and moving Anna Beck to the role of Black Zero, my new personal bodyguard and assistant.

As a postscript, members of Chess Team awarded me with a custom-carved wooden chess piece. It was the same height as the king piece, but with the head of an eagle in flight, representing both my time as a former US Army Ranger, and as a former US President. But mostly, the piece symbolized Chess Team's admiration of my survival abilities and their acceptance of me as a member of the team, and not just as their handler. Unknown to me at the time, I would see far more and far worse action in the field as a member of the team.

Mission 03.8

Designate: CALLSIGN: KING – BLACKOUT

A plan to finally end the threat of Brainstorm coincided with the resurgence of a threat Alexander Diotrephes had long ago dispatched, when the Louvre Museum in Paris happened to be displaying a mock version of the destroyed Afghan Bamiyan Buddhas. Graham Brown orchestrated a Global Energy Future conference in Paris, and King abducted one of the designated special attendees—Bill Downey—taking his place with the aid of a high tech face mask and a voice modification device.

Unfortunately, King's disguise was seen through, and he was captured. Across town, Sara Fogg and Fiona Lane, King's girlfriend and adopted daughter, were enjoying their Parisian holiday, despite King's urgent return to duty, when they spotted Alexander Diotrephes and followed the man to the Louvre. Working under the pseudonym of Albert Carutius, Alexander was setting up a sonic experiment on some of the actual Bamiyan rubble that was accompanying the mock exhibit, which displayed the beauty of the irrevocably lost statues from Afghanistan.

Challenging Brown to a game of chance, King learned that the man was indeed the intelligence behind the so-called computer network, Brainstorm. The man was setting up a new worldwide quantum computer network, with the assistance of internationally renowned Indian hacker Bandar Pradesh. Before King had a chance to escape, Timor Suvorov, Russian Spetsnaz, assaulted the riverboat Brown was using as his headquarters, and kidnapped Brown, leaving King behind.

Unfortunately, Brown's quantum network had already been activated across a series of satellite cellular phones that had been given to guests at the conference. The only way to shut the network down was for King to find all of the guests that had received phones, or get Brown to shut it down. As King chased down the Spetsnaz forces, hoping to retrieve Brown, here in New Hampshire, our systems were suddenly hacked when Brown's network went live. Lewis Aleman and I scrambled to rip the system apart, preventing penetration of our security. But the problems in Paris were only beginning.

A devastating earthquake hit Paris, plunging the city into a blackout. At the Louvre, the loss of power also exposed Sara Fogg, Fiona Lane and Julia Preston, a Global Heritage Commission officer for UNESCO, to the radiation leaking off the Bamiyan rubble—which Alexander had been keeping in check. He revealed that the rubble actually contained a micro black hole.

On the River Seine, King fought the Russian special forces, killing several of their team before absconding with Brown, heading back for Bandar Pradesh, and hopefully a way to shut the computer network down. But Pradesh, a hacker who went by the codename of Shiva, had a completely different agenda from Brown. Consumed by anarchism and ennui, Pradesh sought only the end of the world, with himself along with it. He had woken the black hole intentionally.

Worse, he'd made it sentient.

The original black hole emitted a smaller, traveling black hole creature with tendrils of dark nothingness that attacked the city. King and the Russian forces fought the thing to no avail, as it turned many of them to stone, until they realized that the kinetic energy of bullets was slowing it slightly and the force of an explosion might stop it completely.

At the museum, Alexander urged Fiona to use her abilities with the mother tongue to attempt singing the black hole back to sleep, as had been done once before, centuries earlier. The black hole creature—something akin to a dark basilisk—killed Pradesh and followed King, pursuing the quantum phone King still possessed. Ultimately King was able to fling a bomb into the creature, ending it, but the black hole in the museum was growing and growing.

Graham Brown, in a suicidal move, threw himself into the giant crater in the museum, hoping to take King with him, but King dodged death yet again and Brown was sucked into the hole. Julia Preston helped to save King's life, and despite specific instructions from Alexander, King encouraged Fiona to attempt soothing the black hole her own way.

The gamble paid off, and the black hole reverted to its previously inert status. When the threat ended, they were surprised that there was also no longer any indication of the previously present lethal doses of radiation. One unexpected side effect of the adventure was the reconstitution of the Bamiyan Buddha statues! I'm sure the Louvre had a tough time explaining that one. Much later we learned that Alexander, who slipped out unnoticed, had taken the piece of rubble containing the black hole. It would play a part in a very unusual adventure for King.

Mission 04
Designate: RAGNAROK

When huge energy globes appeared in cities around the world—São Paulo, Karachi, Seoul, Cairo, Los Angeles, and Philadelphia, there was no doubt the cause was something that would involve the Chess Team. The only problem was that we were light, with Rook still AWOL after Siberia, and Queen still in Northern Europe, looking for him. But as it turned out, they were both able to play their parts from the remotest region of Norway.

Knight and Bishop were on assignment in Uganda, staking out the United Faithful Army, an offshoot of Joseph Kony's 'Lord's Resistance Army.' For the first time, I had to abort a mission, and I recalled them when the lightning-shooting spheres appearing around the planet ejected armies of super fast creatures that maimed, killed and abducted civilians. King was on vacation with Sara Fogg and his daughter in Florida, and I had to have a US Ranger team on maneuvers with a Russian helicopter collect him. Naturally, he was far from refreshed, having just stopped a random suicide bomber at the amusement park.

In the strange Norwegian village where Rook had become embroiled in local and supernatural affairs, the entirety of the village suddenly attacked him, as mindless, rage-filled combatants. The woman Rook had rescued on Maksim Dashkov's boat, Asya Machtcenko, arrived in time to assist him, and the villagers abruptly ceased their attacks and wandered away dazed. Shortly afterward,

Queen arrived, and experiencing both relief at finding Rook and frustration at his long absence without contact, she slugged him. To hear Rook tell it, the resulting cat fight between Asya and Queen was something epic.

Knight and Bishop were diverted to Shanghai when yet another devastating energy globe erupted there, and they faced the creatures from the portals—christened 'Dire Wolves' by George Pierce, who was assisting from Endgame's new (and salamander-free) headquarters in New Hampshire. Knight was the first to experience the creatures' sonic cry, which activated a severe panic attack in those who heard it. After a few near misses, they called in an airstrike on the creatures, but the quick beasts fled into their energy dome and it disappeared. The men then headed to London.

King was routed to Chicago to join me in the field, along with a platoon of National Guardsmen. Arriving via a specially modified two-man jet, King's plane was struck by a bolt of lightning from the energy sphere and he had a harrowing ejection, which took him into the sphere, and we learned it was a dimensional portal to...well, to somewhere else.

After a short ground battle, we boarded a flight to New York, to rendezvous with General Keasling and yet another energy globe—only this one was 38 floors off the ground and lodged between two skyscrapers. Once inside the building, we discovered a second secret weapon of the creatures—a pheromone that put King out of commission and into a sleepy stupor.

Knight and Bishop arrived in London in time to engage the Dire Wolves in battle on the London Eye—a

440-foot-tall Ferris wheel on the River Thames. The battle spread to nearby Westminster Bridge, and unfortunately, the Eye toppled (with Bishop riding it down), and Knight was carried into an energy dome by an injured Dire Wolf. Bishop pursued him into the energy vortex, and we initially thought them both lost.

In Norway, Rook, Queen and Asya discovered and infiltrated a previously hidden section of the former Nazi lab Rook had found on his earlier solo adventure. They discovered that Eirek Fossen had created a containment cage to harness one of the energy globes, and to keep it open. He was aware of the side effect globes opening globally, but he was unfazed by them, as he was consumed by religious fervor, worshiping something on the other side of the portal. Queen experienced the fear paralysis of the Dire Wolf roar, but discovered that the creatures were unable to see when the air was filled with particulates—dust, snow or otherwise. It gave her an edge, and she took the fight to the creatures. Asya was affected by the pheromones, similarly to King. She eventually helped to free the captured Rook.

After some hair-raising experiences on the high-rise towers in Manhattan, we snapped King out of his brainwashed delirium, only to discover that he had pitched his backpack nuke into the portal in his stupor—but he had not been able to arm it. Chased by a horde of Dire Wolves, and with the energy globe disappearing and taking down the building, we raced for the roof and barely escaped on a helicopter, in one of the most terrifying stunts I've ever experienced.

Unfortunately, not everyone got out alive.

Our good friend General Michael Keasling lost his life in the tower's collapse. More globes of destruction damaged parts of Kinshasa, Istanbul, Lima, Mumbai and Cape Town. The effect was increasing and would exponentially devour the planet in just a few days.

After consulting with Lewis Aleman and George Pierce in New Hampshire, we realized we needed to get all our forces to Norway, where Rook and Queen were already engaged at ground zero for these other-dimensional incursions. Somewhere on the other side of the dimensional portal, Bishop and Knight miraculously found each other—and Knight had retrieved the backpack nuclear device King had lost.

When Endgame forces arrived in Norway, Rook and Asya were facing off against seemingly endless numbers of Dire Wolves, streaming through the open dimensional portal. The tide of battle turned, but then something else came out of the energy globe. Something huge. Fenrir was some kind of mother to the Dire Wolf creatures, and so named for the giant wolf out of Norse legend. But she didn't look like a wolf. Instead she resembled a giant molten slag of marshmallowy disgusting, and she oozed menace. Bishop and Knight came back into our world, right on her immense heels, placing the vicious creature in a crossfire, but something more desperate would be needed.

We set about destroying the Faraday cage-like structure Fossen's people had created while under Fenrir's influence, a device that contained and stabilized the portal. At the same time, King piloted *Crescent*, the team's supersonic stealth transport plane, in a collision with Fenrir, knocking her back through the portal and escaping with Rook's help, just before we shut down the portal. For good measure, King left the backpack nuke on the other side to detonate. We can only hope that it was enough to finish off Fenrir. But we can be certain that Eirek Fossen, who had ventured to the other dimension, met his demise in the fiery explosion.

The battle had taken its toll, costing us several key support team members, including Matthew Carrack. The only upsides were that Rook and Queen finally acted upon the feelings they had for one another, and King and Asya realized they were siblings, intentionally kept apart by their Russian spy parents. The same parents who had been missing since they had slipped away from Lewis Aleman in North Carolina.

When we returned to Endgame HQ with the plans for Fossen's dimensional stabilizer, they were promptly stolen, and a note left in their place. It was signed with the symbol of the Herculean Society, and the sender claimed to be holding King's parents hostage, to prevent him from meddling in the Society's affairs. King vowed to find Alexander Diotrephes, and to kill him.

Mission 05
Designate: OMEGA

King and his sister, Asya, set off to find their parents. It was a strange experience for King. The sister he had known and grown up with, Julie, had died in a military training accident, spurring his own decision to join the Army. Now he suddenly had another sister. He had no idea just how strange his journey would become, however.

While the rest of the team was destroying a chemical weapons plant in North Korea, King and Asya followed a clue about the Herculean Society to a library in Malta, where they found Society files on Manifold Genetics, indicating that Ridley had owned a lab in Tunisia, but it was now under Society control. They also faced off against some of Alexander's wraith-like creatures, who seemed reluctant to injure King.

When the rest of the team returned to Endgame, we found intruders waiting for us—and all three of them looked exactly like Richard Ridley. His last remaining mother tongue-created duplicates revealed their certainty that the original Ridley was alive and being held captive, and that the man behind it all was Alexander Diotrephes. When we were unconvinced, the dupes showed us footage at the Louvre from a lone, still functioning security camera that had captured Alexander stealing the miniature black hole. Making a deal with the devil—or several devils—the team set out with the duplicates for North Africa. It was coincidentally the same facility where King and Asya were bound. Although after what happened there, I question anything that smells of coincidence.

Following a series of clues, King and Asya found the Manifold lab, under a major mosque on the edge of the Carthage ruins. They quickly faced off against a huge number of the wraiths, which Alexander had called The Forgotten, but once again the creatures refrained from injuring King, allowing him passage to where Alexander was waiting for them. When they found him, King charged the man, and the two came to blows.

The rest of the team and the duplicates arrived just moments afterward, and were unaware that a large military force was waiting in the ruins for Chess Team to enter the lab, before springing their trap. Once inside, the team, along with the duplicates, found the still living, decapitated remains of Richard Ridley, who was being held in an inhuman array of cages that prevented his body parts from rejoining and regenerating. Thinking him the lesser of two evils, the team helped to free Ridley, and they were rewarded for the effort by betrayal. The duplicates trapped the team and escaped with Richard Ridley, just as Darius Ridley's mercenary forces invaded the underground base.

Peter and Lynn Sigler were actually fine, and voluntarily staying with Alexander, who explained that he had obtained all of the fringe technology in his lab for the most noble of purposes: for love. Before King could stop him, Alexander propelled himself and King into a small, contained energy portal like the one Chess Team had faced in Norway. The men vanished, and the lab exploded, the devastation witnessed by Asya, who thought her brother dead.

The truth would be far stranger.

Chess Team fought a protracted battle inside the Manifold *Omega* lab, constantly pinned by Darius's forces, until Rook broke the stalemate with a suicidal ploy that flooded the base, allowing the sea to rush in through an underwater gallery window Ridley had set up for observation of a very unusual archeological find—the submerged Colossus of Rhodes. We would later learn that Alexander had arranged for its relocation after an earthquake had toppled it in Greece, back in 226 BC.

But what Ridley was about to do with the statue would beggar the imagination, using his mother tongue ability to animate the statue and have it rise from the floor of the sea and stand—while Rook was stuck on its head, 300 feet off the ground. The resulting battle between Chess Team, the massive statue, Ridley's duplicates and Darius's mutinous forces who were intent on destroying the intruders and killing Richard Ridley, was enough to rouse the local Presidential Guard, creating even more havoc on the battlefield. Chess Team's salvation was to come from a most unexpected source—the seemingly exploded King, who returned to the battle field with an army of The Forgotten on his side.

As King later related to us, the portal had propelled him and Alexander not to another dimension, but still within ours and back in time. *Way* back in time, to 799 BC. Alexander had spent decades collecting the necessary scientific equipment to make the trip back in time, to save Acca Larentia, the love of his life, from an accidental death at the hands of the Forgotten in Alexander's laboratory. Initially outraged, King gave in and agreed to help Alexander in his noble quest. But the job necessitated King being slipped an herbal concoction that would help him to heal from any injury, and which would even resurrect him upon death. King had become, like Alexander, an immortal.

Alexander revealed all, explaining how he had fooled Richard Ridley with promises of the location of a powerful weapon, the Chest of Adoon, which was actually just a small airtight box containing some of Alexander's belongings, left behind in Carthage in the past. He explained how the Siglers, and thus King and Asya, were actually descendents of Alexander, which explained their unusual immunity to the Dire Wolf roars in Norway. Over time, the man explained his plan for using Richard Ridley's mother tongue to make a duplicate of Acca, which the younger Alexander could discover dead in his lab, while the true Acca could be kept safe by the time-traveling Alexander. There was just one problem—the job would take years to accomplish, as they had arrived decades before Acca's death.

King left a surprise for Ridley in the Chest of Adoon, which would remain undisturbed through time until the battle that was waging in Chess Team's present. He then embarked on a series of adventures with Alexander, until the two successfully saved Acca's life. That was when Alexander unveiled his final surprise: he was not from our world, but from a different dimension himself, and he wished to return to it, reunited with his wife. To send them home would mean stranding King in the past, doomed to live out the centuries as an immortal, until he could rejoin Chess Team in the present. But as Alexander revealed, King never really had any choice in the matter, he had already decided to do so, because the centuries older King had been friends with Alexander for decades, before Chess Team first encountered Alexander in Gibraltar. It was the ancient King who had stolen the dimensional stabilizer plans from Endgame, on Alexander's behalf, and even the ancient King that had rescued Fiona at Siletz. Fate, it seemed, had already been determined. King sent Alexander and Acca home, then lived out the years until it was time for him to exact his revenge on Richard Ridley.

Arriving in time to turn the tide of the battle with the Forgotten, the wraiths now loyal to King, he engaged Richard Ridley in a martial showdown that left the other members of Chess Team flabbergasted. Until, in a last minute bid for ultimate power, Ridley opened the Chest of Adoon, seeking to unleash the power it contained. To Ridley's surprise, and his demise, the airtight Chest contained a fragmentation grenade King had left for him, centuries earlier.

Richard Ridley was no more, and to make certain of it, King buried the man's savagely mutilated, severed head in the very same tomb where Alexander had originally buried the Lernaean Hydra's head—under a massive stone in Nazca, the driest place on Earth. The story, as well as Jack Sigler, had come full circle.

Mission 06
Designate: SAVAGE

The threat of Richard Ridley firmly neutralized, we thought the worst days were behind us. But as we resumed dealing with more normal threats like terrorists and coup d'états, we had no idea what the team was in for.

With King still, understandably, acting different after his return to us in Tunisia, Chess Team mobilized to retrieve a small nuclear device, from a terrorist in Egypt. Unfortunately, despite the use of new technology—quantum-linked phones and glasses connected to the same quantum network featuring automated targeting systems—the team was seconds late in stopping Hadir al-Shahri, the Yemeni terrorist, from being slaughtered. The nuke fell into unknown hands.

Back in the United States, Domenick Boucher, the team's inside man in government, was about to retire from his position as the Director of Central Intelligence. Days before he was done, President Chambers sought his aid with a situation in the Democratic Republic of the Congo. Their president, Joseph Mulamba, had left the country on a personal mission to England, where he was kidnapped. In his absence, General Patrice Velle was poised to seize power from the interim president, with the assistance of French mercenary Monique Favreau and the money of Consolidated Energy, a multinational company with deep pockets and Washington political backing. Only later did we learn that the US political clout came from Utah Senator Lance Marrs, the same man who had been a thorn in my side during the mother tongue fiasco.

Boucher asked for Chess Team's help, and we agreed, Rook and Queen heading to England to search for Mulamba, while Bishop and Knight went to Lake Kivu to help stabilize the region. King and Asya Machtcenko, now operating under the callsign: Pawn, went to Kinshasa to liaise with interim President Gerard Okoa. They didn't have a chance to view the part of the city damaged in the Dire Wolf attack two years earlier, before General Jean-Claude Mabuki, chief of the President's Republican Guard, met with them to offer his assistance and welcome them. Mabuki would become a good ally.

Near Lake Kivu, Bishop and Knight landed in the thick of it, with rebels slaughtering a scientific camp. The only survivor turned out to be someone King had encountered before—Dr. Felice Carter. Before she could reveal that detail to Bishop and Knight though, they were hit with a mortar attack.

In England, Rook and Queen tracked Mulamba down to a farmhouse in Kent. After a brief firefight with the mercenaries holding him, Queen and Rook liberated Mulamba, but the man refused to leave the continent and go back to Africa. Apparently he had been following clues that indicated Henry Morton Stanley had found something in the heart of the Congo, while infamously searching for Dr. David Livingstone. Something he'd torn from his journals. Mulamba believed it was evidence of an ancient, highly developed African society—the birthplace of humanity—something he felt would give his countrymen the self esteem to rise beyond petty territorial squabbles and move into the twenty-first century. He convinced Rook and Queen to take him to a museum in Belgium, seeking the missing pages of Stanley's journal.

Back in the Congo, Knight was horribly maimed in the resulting mortar explosion, a long piece of metal obliterating his left eye. Bishop, Carter and Knight fled from the rebels into the jungle. Meanwhile, in the capital, Okoa was reluctant to accept help from King and Pawn, and Favreau captured them using regular Army troops—not Mabuki's Republican Guard, who were still loyal to Mulamba, despite his absence. Favreau attempted to interrogate King and Pawn, but then sent them out into the jungle to be executed. King and Pawn effected a last-minute escape, and were able to rejoin Mabuki's forces, just as the country was erupting in Civil War. Velle and Favreau had taken Okoa hostage.

Rook and Queen took Mulamba to Belgium and they found the pages from the journal—but not before Favreau's mercenaries tracked them down at the Royal Museum for Central Africa. The gunfight was brief, before *Crescent II* collected them from the roof, but the damage had been done. Mulamba had been fatally wounded. With his dying breath, he beseeched Rook to track down the lost city in Africa. The journal pages pointed to Lake Natron, in Tanzania.

Bishop unintentionally ruined things for a jungle village, when he protected them from bullying rebels. The villagers fled before rebel reprisals might start. Their village elder, a man named David, escorted Bishop, Knight and Carter to what he thought would be safety.

A cavern he had discovered in the 1960s that contained living, breathing dinosaurs—small velociraptors. After an initial skirmish with the creatures, Bishop came to see that the cavern would be the perfect place to evade the pursuing rebels.

King and Pawn set the Republican Guard against Favreau's forces in a bid to rescue Okoa, but Favreau revealed her trump card—the nuke she had stolen from under Chess Team's noses in Egypt. She then shot Pawn and made her escape. King rushed his sister outside and stole a GAZ Tigr, an all-purpose armored infantry vehicle. Once again, King was able to rendezvous with General Mabuki, and the man obtained medical aid for Pawn.

Rook and Queen went diving in special drysuits into the alkaline lake in Tanzania, discovering a submerged tunnel and evidence of an ancient civilization. But when Queen was swept away in a current, Rook followed her, the two traveling hundreds of miles in the current through the darkness. The strange cavern system eventually brought them under Rwanda and back into the Congo—connecting with the very dinosaur filled cavern Bishop and Knight were in. They had found continued evidence of civilization all through the extensive tunnel system, and Bishop, Knight and Carter had found several more species of ancient creatures, uncatalogued by modern man. Carter pieced together the facts that there was an entire self-contained ecosystem under the ground, all hinging on extremophile microbes that created the rich natural gas deposits under the Congo.

King arrived at the cavern, stunned to meet Felice Carter there. Although the woman had been using a variety of techniques to control the power within her, King understandably sidelined her—but not before she and Bishop had bonded through their experience in the jungle and with witnessing Knight's injury. While Knight was given medical aid, the others proceeded to a camp near Lake Kivu to confront Velle and Favreau. Too late to stop her, Chess Team explained to Velle that he had been a patsy in Favreau's larger scheme. The woman took her nuke out over the lake, intending to submerge it and destroy the region's rich natural gas reserves. Reluctantly, Okoa, who had signed over power to Velle while under duress, and the general agreed to work together and with Chess Team to try to stop Monique Favreau. But they never got the opportunity.

Erik Somers—Bishop—took matters into his own hands, flying off in a helicopter and chasing Favreau down. After dropping the helicopter on top of Favreau, Bishop dove deep into the waters of the lake to prevent the bomb from reaching its specified detonation depth. We know he succeeded, because the bomb was eventually found—undetonated. But no sign of the man could be found. King and the others did find the injured, but alive Favreau, though, and they quickly dispatched her.

We searched the lake and the surrounding area for weeks, but no sign of Erik Somers was ever found. A private memorial service was held for him in Illinois with his adopted parents and his birth mother, Faiza Abbasi. After the attendees left, Chess Team held an even more private ceremony, and in addition to bidding farewell to Erik Somers, we promoted Asya Machtcenko to the role and callsign of Bishop. She continues to illustrate her worth in the role, as she strives to be true to the memory of the man who saved millions of lives by giving his.

Felice Carter remained in Africa working on the extremophile for a very long time. I monitored the situation for a while, before I lost track of her. I also explored reports of a giant man running through the jungle, but they were all inconclusive. Not enough actionable intel. Could be anything, really. Probably just wishful thinking on my part.

Mission 06a
Designate: CONTINUUM

King was propelled back in time during the Omega fiasco in Tunisia. He ended up living from 799 BC to the present, with the help of some of Alexander Diotrephes's chemical and herbal ministrations, which kept him from aging—and even resurrected him after death—during those long years. And yes, that means there would have been two Kings on the planet for a few decades. Time travel makes my damn head hurt. For the sake of labeling, I'm referring to that period in his life as the *Continuum*. For 2,814 years, King traveled the globe, righting wrongs but generally attempting to stay out of the history books. He hasn't told me much about that time in his past, and his claims that he hardly remembers much of it seem genuine. I can barely recall my own childhood, just a few decades ago. I can only imagine what it must be like surviving for *millennia*.

Still, King has actually let slip a few items regarding his travels through the years. Each mention or aside draws my attention and further intrigues me. When I have a chance, I really need to get him to tell me as much of it as he will.

He referenced a time in Babylon with the heir-apparent and a fallen alien craft, supposedly the home of the goddess Tiamat. It was, according to King, responsible for nearly terra-forming the planet. He talked about his time on the Mediterranean with Alexander, which took up the first twenty-odd years of his sojourn through time. It was during that time that he first died and was resurrected by Alexander's strange concoction of herbs. I suspect the brew was not dissimilar from the Hydra DNA we saw a few years ago. I tried to press King for more information about the plants in question, but he evaded the topic. He usually shuts down further discussion by simply pointing out that the plants used are now extinct.

Shortly after his return to us in Carthage, when he arrived with a posse of half-dead, wraithlike creatures willing to do battle for him, I noticed that King was wearing an unusual wristwatch. When I asked him about it, he revealed that the 1967 stainless-steel Omega Speedmaster Professional was a gift from American astronaut Buzz Aldrin. If I'm not mistaken, that would make it the first watch that was worn on the Moon, as Aldrin wore it outside his spacesuit during his EVA on the lunar surface. Unfortunately, that discussion with King took place just prior to Chess Team's departure for the Congo, and we were busy with funeral arrangements after that mess. I never got to ask him for more details about how the watch came to be in his possession.

Among the other gems that have cropped up in brief conversations were his attendance at the first Olympic games in 776 BC, which he claims to still remember clearly. He was involved in some kind of a piracy episode with the emperor of the Chinese Zhou dynasty. He fought in the American Revolutionary War as a Minuteman, and he visited Roanoke Island before the colony's mysterious disappearance. He spent part of World War II in the Himalaya, and he was a Roman

Legionnaire at the Fall of Constantinople. He's said little about his experiences in the Middle Ages or about the Renaissance.

All I know for sure is he fought in wars as a nameless soldier and he has led armies. He orchestrated coups and fought evil. I'd have expected no less of him, even though he knew he was unable to change the major events of history as he traveled through them.

He has also lived many anonymous lives, farming and even herding sheep. He traveled all over the world, speaks dozens of languages now and has a surprising amount of knowledge on a wide variety of topics, as if his interests in academia and trivia grew with each passing year he was trapped in the past.

One day, I hope he'll tell me a little of everything.

From a strategic perspective, I'm most concerned about his activities in the late 20th and early 21st centuries and whatever ramifications they might have in the present day, for the team and for our plans. The last thing we need now is a new enemy to come out of nowhere.

EPILOGUE: RENDITION

"Is that really all you have to say?" Rudin shoved her chair back from the desk and crossed her legs, the fabric of her suit hugging her curves.

Tom Duncan shifted in his hard wooden chair again. The gleaming stainless steel handcuffs on his wrists rattled with the effort. He tried for a minute to push the sleeves of his scratchy orange jumpsuit up on his forearms a little. The material didn't breathe very well, and it was warm in the interrogation room.

Rudin sat staring at him, waiting for him to reply. They'd been chatting for hours. She knew from his long silences on topics he was unwilling to discuss that it might take him a while to parse his responses, or he just might keep silent. Either way, she had learned to wait a while before wasting breath reiterating questions.

"That's what you needed to hear. Chess Team was a required element of national and world security. When conventional US forces were helpless to stop the obliteration of cities around the world, we ended the threat. When the Brugada virus was running rampant because of a bioterrorist—and it even took my life before the Secret Service brought me back—we found and eliminated the threat. You might not have known you needed us, Ms. Rudin, but Dom knew it. And so did President Chambers. When he needed plausible deniability in stopping that fiasco in the Congo last year—which Marrs had a hand in creating, mind you, or when he needed someone to take down the El Sol cartel in Mexico, the President called Dom. Dom called me."

Rudin stood slowly. "You're saying we needed you, and that we still need you."

"That's exactly what I'm saying."

"Come with me," she said, and she stood, pulled on her jacket and started for the door.

Duncan got to his feet, the coarse fabric of the orange jumpsuit chaffing as it always did. He ran a hand through the thick beard on his face, the handcuffs clanking as he did so. Then he followed Rudin out into the hallway. It was as nondescript as the room they had just left. She led him past three doors—the first two he hadn't seen opened, and the third was the door to the small room that had been his home for the last six weeks. If he'd been keeping track properly. He had no clocks, no watches, no calendar, no writing implements and no windows. He wasn't sure when it was day or night, but someone brought him three meals a day and slid them through the slot at the bottom of his room's door. The room wasn't terrible. It had an adjacent private bathroom with a toilet, tub and a shower, although there was no mirror. The towels were replaced daily through the slot, and they were at least as nice as any you'd find in a chain hotel. The food wasn't five-star, but neither was it a mash and gruel. Yesterday had been a pretty good steak and a salad.

He did calisthenics and he worked his way through the books on the bookshelf in the room. Classic literary novels and modern action thrillers. Nothing with any hint of a political bent, he'd noticed. Rudin had been his first visitor. At least they weren't torturing him.

Not yet, anyway.

At the end of the corridor was a door with a wire-reinforced window leading to a gray metal staircase. Duncan followed Rudin into the stairwell, and up the steps. Looking up the center, he guess they were about ten stories down. They ascended in silence, and as they went up, Duncan realized there were no other floors. The occasional fire extinguisher was bolted to the wall, but that was it.

Rudin was slowing by the time they had ascended eight levels. Duncan was pleased to note that even though he hadn't been able to aerobically exercise for a while, he was still in good enough shape that he wasn't winded yet.

At the top was another door with a wire window. This one had a mechanical cipher lock at the side. The old kind Duncan had seen in US embassies abroad. A stainless steel rectangle with five buttons and side panels to conceal the code as the user typed them in. Rudin rapidly hit a pattern on the buttons, shielding them with her hand as she did so. Duncan had watched closely, but he wouldn't even be able to hazard a guess at the code.

A loud *thunk* signified a deep lock retracting from the door. Rudin opened the door and stepped through. Duncan followed, and immediately squeezed his eyes shut against the glare.

"You'll need a minute to adjust," she said. "Here."

He felt her placing something in his hand, and he recognized the feel of the plastic sunglasses. He raised his chained hands up and placed the plastic frames on his face, then cracked his eyes.

He was in a small glassed-in room, with a solid wall to the right, which held a row of pegs. Hanging on the pegs were massive fur-hooded parkas and snow pants. There was a low table with gloves and hats, and along the front windowed wall was a neat row of insulated winter boots and a small backpack. The only other thing in the room was a huge propane-powered heater that was struggling to keep the room warm.

It was the view outside the windows that captivated Duncan's attention, though.

Snow.

For as far as the eye could see.

A few nearby antenna towers—missing their radio antennas—broke the monotony, and a steel-framed trellis rose up from the ground a few feet from their windows. In the distance, there were some low hills, snuggled under a pale blue sky.

It wasn't what Duncan had been expecting. He'd thought he was at Guantanamo Bay detention camp, the notorious US military prison in Cuba. They'd drugged him and moved him in his sleep. He'd had no idea where, but Cuba had been logical.

"Where...?"

"You're in the tiny hamlet of Alert, Canada," Rudin told him, as she stared out at the endless vista of snow. "Formerly a population of five. Now officially zero. We're at the northern tip of Nunavut. Roughly 500 miles from the North Pole. The nearest city is Iqaluit. About 1300 miles—" She walked across the small glassed-in room and pointed to the right. "—that way."

Duncan looked where she had pointed, and the view remained the same. An endless panorama of brilliant white under baby blue, barely clouded sky. "I didn't know we had any detention sites in Canada."

"This one is just for you. It used to be a Canadian weather and radio receiving station, but all the tech has been removed. The Canadian government leased the site to us two years ago, when the cost of heating the facility just became too much for them."

"Pretty cold outside?" Duncan ventured.

"The average high is six degrees above zero. Snow ten months of the year. There's an airstrip, but it's often unusable. That's why it took me so long to come visit you."

Duncan turned to Rudin, looking at her through the sunglasses. "You said this place was just for me?"

"Yes. There's nothing electronic here. Not even a toothbrush. No RFID chips anywhere. I had to leave my cellphone in Washington before coming up here. In other words—there's no way for Jack Sigler and his small band of stragglers to track you down, up here. And you won't be getting out on your own. It's over 2500 miles to Quebec."

Duncan removed the sunglasses, squinting as he did so, but he wanted to look at Rudin's face—at her eyes—without the tinting.

He needed to look for that glint. That spark. That tiny little sign that Danielle Rudin might actually become an ally instead of his jailer. He'd seen it downstairs in the interrogation room. He was sure of it.

Now he wasn't so certain.

"There's no security besides the locks on the doors," she said. He knew that wasn't entirely true, because he'd noticed the young Washington agent with the shoulder-holstered weapon, but maybe he was just Rudin's escort. He hadn't seen anyone else in the prison, although someone was clearly supplying him food and clean linens, and taking away the dirty. "You said we needed you, and that we still do. That's going to be a little difficult. You'll be here for the rest of your life, Mr. Duncan. You were tried in absentia, in a closed and private trial. And that's the last time I'm officially allowed to refer to you by your former title. Moving forward, we'll simply refer to you as a number."

"'I am not a number. I am a free man.'" Duncan quoted the controversial 1960s television show *The Prisoner* with a sad resignation on his face.

Understanding the reference, Rudin looked at him with compassion. "There have been sixteen people actually convicted of treason against the United States of America. We don't count Governor Thomas Dorr in 1844, because his verdict was annulled ten years later."

"Making me..." Duncan began.

"Welcome to the village, Number Seventeen."

She moved to the wall and started to put on her snow pants and parka, slipping off her shoes and placing them in the backpack.

Duncan watched her until she had donned her snow boots and was headed for the door to the outside of the windowed room.

"You should get inside and head downstairs. It's going to be incredibly cold when I open the door. I'll be back in a few months. Can I get you anything?"

"A chess set would be nice."

Rudin smiled at him again, and he saw that tiny, faint, glorious glimmer of hope once again in her eyes. "I'll see what I can do."

CONFIDENTIAL INFORMATION

DATE:	2014	ORIGINATOR:	DEEP BLUE

SUBJECT:

ILLUSTRATIONS

DATE	ACTION	INITIAL
	ORIGINAL DOCUMENTS	
	ENDGAME'S OWN GRAPHIC DESIGNER,	
	CHRISTIAN GULDAGER, HAS PROVIDED	
	IMAGES FOR THE TEAM AND FOR SOME OF	
	THE THREATS WE'VE FACED. FOR OBVIOUS	
	REASONS, WE DON'T WANT ACTUAL	
	PHOTOS OF THE TEAM MEMBERS TO	
	ACCOMPANY THESE FILES. WHEN IN THE	
	FIELD, IT ISN'T ALWAYS POSSIBLE TO	
	CAPTURE PHOTOGRAPHIC EVIDENCE OF	
	SOME OF THE FOES THE TEAM HAS	
	ENCOUNTERED.	
	DB	

KING

QUEEN

ROOK

BISHOP

(K.I.A.)

KNIGHT

BISHOP

LEWIS ALEMAN

DEEP
BLUE

DR.
SARA
FOGG

FIONA
LANE-SIGLER

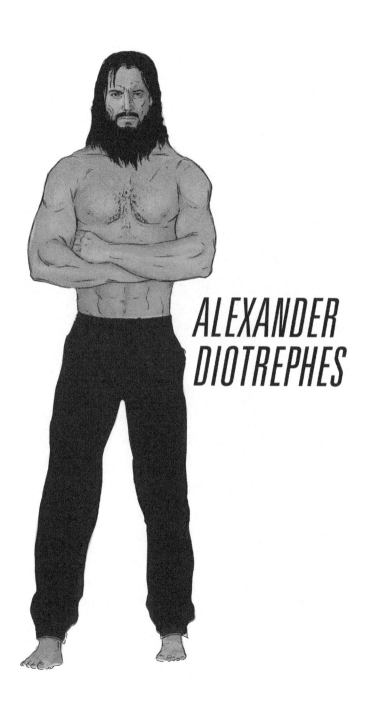

ALEXANDER
DIOTREPHES

THE LERNAEAN HYDRA

RICHARD RIDLEY

DR. ANTHONY WESTON

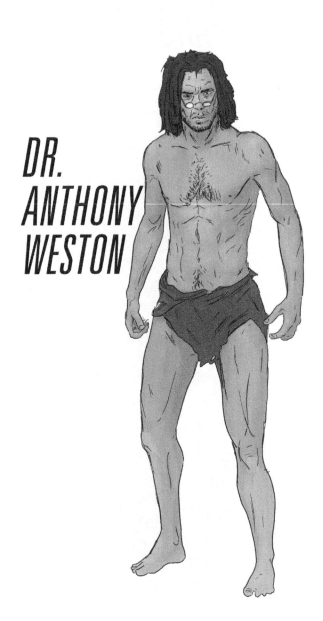

LUCY WESTON
(HYBRID)

THE RHINO GOLEM

DIRE WOLF

FENRIR

THE FORGOTTEN

THE
COLOSSUS
OF
RHODES

DATE	ORIGINATOR:
2014	DEEP BLUE

SUBJECT:

EYE WITNESS SKETCHES

DATE	ACTION	INITIAL
	ORIGINAL DOCUMENTS	
	OVER THE YEARS, WE'VE COLECTED MANY EYE WITNESS SKETCHES OF CREATURES AND FOES THE TEAM HAS FACED. EACH OF THESE IMAGES WAS SKETCHED BY A BYSTANDER, OR IN SOME CASES BY AN ENDGAME MEMBER AFTER CHESS TEAM RETURNED HOME.	
	LEWIS ALEMAN	

KNIGHT & BISHOP

(Sketched by Anja Kesting,
as described by Lewis Aleman)

ROOK & QUEEN

(Sketched by Anja Kesting,
as described by Lewis Aleman)

'FRANKENSTEINS'

(Sketched by Anja Kesting,
as described by Lewis Aleman)

RED

(Sketched by
Jeremy Robinson,
as described
by Rook)

NGUOI RUNG

(Sketched by Jeremy Robinson,
as described by Queen)

QUEEN'S BRAND

(Sketched by Kyle Mohr)

STONEHENGE GOLEM

(Sketched by Jeff Sexton)

GOLEM SKELETON

(Sketched by Jeremy Robinson, as described by Knight)

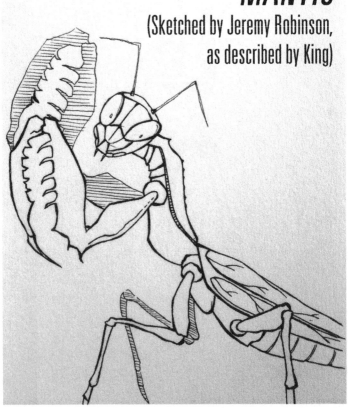

DESERT MANTIS

(Sketched by Jeremy Robinson,
as described by King)

KNIGHT
(Sketched by
Sabu Schmatz)

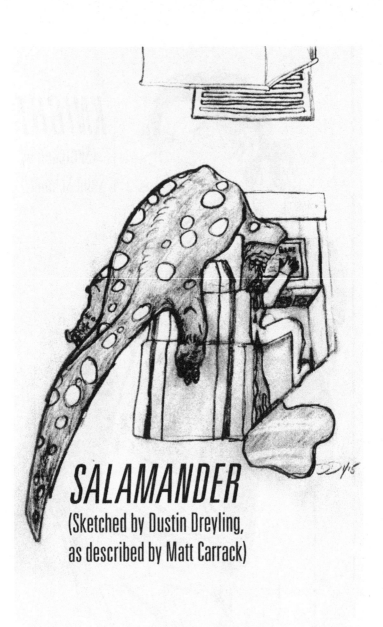

SALAMANDER
(Sketched by Dustin Dreyling,
as described by Matt Carrack)

KNIGHT & BISHOP

(Sketched by Anja Kesting,
as described by Lewis Aleman)

DIRE WOLF
(Sketched by Pixie Brearley)

KNIGHT & BISHOP (Sketched by Anja Kesting, as described by Lewis Aleman)

DIRE WOLF
(Sketched by Zach Cole)

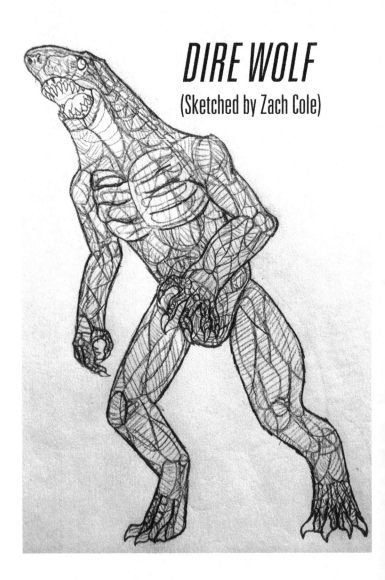

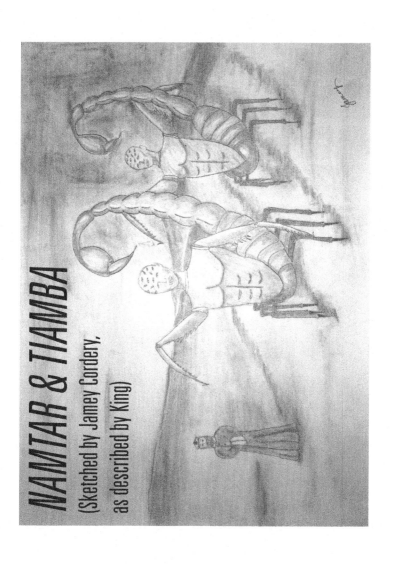

NAMTAR & TIAMBA

(Sketched by Jamey Cordery, as described by King)

TIAMAT

(Sketched by Kent Holloway,
as described by King)

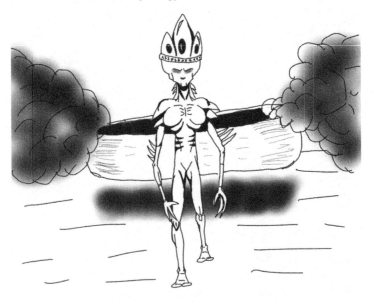

BIBLIOGRAPHY

Book 0: *Prime* (with Sean Ellis)
This prequel novel, written in 2013, shows the epic fight between King and Queen, the formation of the Chess Team and the injury that took Lewis Aleman out of the field. It also hints at the team's future confrontations with Richard Ridley.

Book 1: *Pulse*
The original Chess Team novel, published in 2009, this story sets up the long Alexander Diotrephes story arc, and introduces Richard Ridley, Gen-Y, the Hydra, Manifold Genetics and the Alpha laboratory, which would become Chess Team's headquarters at the end of *Threshold*.

Book 2: *Instinct*
This novel, published in 2010, introduced readers to Sara Fogg and, briefly, to Fiona Lane. It also was the novel where the team learned the identity of their mysterious handler, Deep Blue, while on a mission deep in the jungles of Vietnam.

Book 3: *Threshold*
Published in 2011, this novel let the creatures off the chain, as Richard Ridley returned, enacting his master plan to acquire the mother tongue—the human protolanguage pre-dating the Tower of Babel story. Seemingly an end to

the Ridley arc, the novel finishes with many loose ends for King's family and with Rook missing in Asia.

The Chesspocalypse

This series of 'Callsign' novellas (shorter books roughly 1/3 to 1/2 the length of a full Chess Team novel) was envisioned as a treat for fans during what we knew would be a long wait after *Threshold* and before *Ragnarok*. Originally meant to be five novellas—one for each major team member—the series grew organically when Sean Ellis had ideas to make the *Callsign: King* story into a trilogy, and when Kane Gilmour suggested Jeremy write a story for Deep Blue without a co-author. He instead asked Kane to co-write it. Each novella is a self-contained tale, and highlights one member of the team, allowing for a small adventure and a more in-depth examination of a single character.

Callsign: King (with Sean Ellis)

The first installment of a trilogy of stories in which King faces the threat known as Brainstorm. In this story, King rescues Sara Fogg and meets Felice Carter, a woman who would play a larger part in Chess Team history, after this first story in which she unknowingly threatens all of humanity.

This novella forms a trilogy with *Underworld* and *Blackout*, and all three titles are collected in *Callsign King: The Brainstorm Trilogy*.

Callsign: Queen (with David Wood)

In this solo outing, Queen goes up against Russian werewolf-like creatures and an amusement park filled with deathtraps, all orchestrated by a man with deep connections to Richard Ridley.

The *Queen* novella is collected with *Rook* and *Bishop* in *Callsign – Tripleshot*.

Callsign: Rook (with Edward G. Talbot)
After a disastrous mission in Siberia, Rook wanders Norway seeking isolation, but he encounters a long buried Nazi lab and a creature very similar to a yeti or Bigfoot. When things go sideways, Rook does what he does best—unleashes destruction.

The *Rook* novella is collected with *Queen* and *Bishop* in *Callsign – Tripleshot*.

Callsign: King 2 – Underworld (with Sean Ellis)
King and George Pierce travel to Arizona to investigate the Mogollon Monsters of legend, while a Russian assassin attempts to track and kill King. What they find is an alternative energy scheme—orchestrated by none other than the Brainstorm network King had faced before in Africa—that has the potential to unravel itself, destroying the planet's atmosphere in the process.

Underworld forms a trilogy with the first *Callsign: King* novella and *Blackout*, and all three titles are collected in *Callsign King: The Brainstorm Trilogy*.

Callsign: Bishop (with David McAfee)
Called to Iran to investigate an old Manifold Genetics lab and a fungal bioweapon on the loose, Bishop also must confront his newly revealed birth parents.

The *Bishop* novella is collected with *Queen* and *Rook* in *Callsign – Tripleshot*.

Callsign: Knight (with Ethan Cross)
Called into China to investigate a Hydra-related threat, Knight teams up with Anna Beck from *Pulse* to stop a madman and his drug-fueled schemes of glory that result in yet another genetic monstrosity—this time in an abandoned city.

The *Knight* and *Deep Blue* novellas are collected in *Callsign – Doubleshot*.

Callsign: Deep Blue (with Kane Gilmour)
While setting up the team's new headquarters, Deep Blue and a few support personnel must weather an attack by Gen-Y mercenaries and an army of mutated, regenerating salamanders the size of African crocodiles, all while trapped in their own base, and with a time-bomb ticking down to destruction.

The *Knight* and *Deep Blue* novellas are collected in *Callsign – Doubleshot*.

Callsign: King 3 – Blackout (with Sean Ellis)
The final installment in the Brainstorm Trilogy showed

us the end of Graham Brown and set the groundwork for a very important event in the lives of King and Alexander, later on in *Omega*.

Blackout forms a trilogy with the first *Callsign: King* novella and *Underworld*, and all three titles are collected in *Callsign King: The Brainstorm Trilogy*.

Book 4: *Ragnarok* (with Kane Gilmour)
Giant balls of energy and lightning open up in cities around the world, devouring chunks of the landscape and unleashing devilishly fast creatures dubbed 'Dire Wolves.' Chess Team, fractured by the loss of Rook and the temporarily absent Queen, must reunite and stop the threat, which originated in the strange town Rook found himself in during his solo novella. The battle rages all over the planet—and even into another dimension.

Book 5: *Omega* (with Kane Gilmour)
Gaining a sister he hadn't known about, King sets out to find his missing parents, while the rest of Chess Team are asked for help from a most unusual trio of intruders into their base. Chess Team travels to Tunisia to stop Alexander Diotrephes—but the legendary Hercules has plans of his own, and they involve the death of Jack Sigler. Tying up the loose threads of all the previous stories, *Omega* was both an epic showdown and a new beginning, but in a very unexpected direction.

Continuum 1: *Guardian* (with J. Kent Holloway)
This short novel was the start of a new series called the *Jack*

Sigler Continuum, and takes place after King had lived in the past for over two hundred years. In the story, he protects the prince of the Babylonian empire from a twisted high priest and the ancient goddess Tiamat, who is not at all what she seems.

Each story in the *Continuum* series will be a standalone adventure and a great jumping-on point for new readers. At the time of this publication, Jeremy and Kent were hard at work on a second title for this new series.

Book 6: *Savage* (with Sean Ellis)
Envisioned as a new jumping on point for readers after *Omega* effectively wrapped up most of the loose story threads from all the previous books, this novel sees the team dealing with the ramifications of King's excursion through time and a brand new adversary, set in a place they've never been: the jungles of the Congo. We also bid farewell to a fan-favorite team member.

Book 7: *Cannibal* (with Sean Ellis)
Recently released, this novel promises to be the most controversial of the series, and this guidebook's narrative serves as a kind of tie-in to events that will affect the team in *Cannibal*, as they battle a rogue drug cartel with a dark secret. The team also faces an epidemic outbreak and a rampaging army of deadly creatures, while forces within the US government are seeking their heads.

"Show of Force" (with Kane Gilmour)
This short story featuring the Chess Team is slated to

appear in *SNAFU II: Survival of the Fittest*, a 2015 military-horror anthology from Cohesion Press. The story will take place after the events in *Cannibal*. The team, still dealing with the ramifications of what happened in Mexico and North Carolina, will be visiting the Gobi Desert and confronting a horror out of legend.

Crossovers

The Chess Team has also popped up briefly (or in mention), in a variety of Jeremy's other titles. Mirabelle Whitney references the events of *Threshold* when speaking to Solomon Ull Vincent in *The Last Hunter – Onslaught*. Milos Vesely glimpses a vision of those same events with the golems in *Nazi Hunter: Atlantis* (formerly titled *I Am Cowboy*), when the bell transports him through different dimensions. Queen makes a cameo appearance in the shadows, speaking to Jon Hudson in *Project Maigo*, after the events of *Ragnarok*. King bumps into Dr. David Goodman from *The Didymus Contingency* in *Omega*, when King is in the past with Alexander. There are more references like these scattered throughout Jeremy's body of work, with many more to come.

CHESS TEAM
READING ORDER CHECKLIST

Prime

Pulse

Instinct

Threshold

Callsign: King

Callsign: Queen

Callsign: Rook

Callsign: King 2 – Underworld

Callsign: Bishop

Callsign: Knight

Callsign: Deep Blue

Callsign: King 3 – Blackout

Ragnarok

Omega

Guardian

Savage

Endgame (Guidebook)

Cannibal

"Show of Force" (short story)

ABOUT THE AUTHORS

Jeremy Robinson is the international bestselling author of fifty novels and novellas including *Uprising*, *Island 731*, *SecondWorld*, the Jack Sigler thriller series, and *Project Nemesis*, the highest selling original (non-licensed) kaiju novel of all time. He's known for mixing elements of science, history and mythology, which has earned him the #1 spot in Science Fiction and Action-Adventure, and secured him as the top creature feature author. The Jack Sigler Thrillers, starting with *Pulse*, are now in development as a feature film series with director Jabbar Raisani, whose work on Game of Thrones earned him an Emmy Award.

Robinson is also known as the bestselling horror writer, Jeremy Bishop, author of *The Sentinel* and the controversial novel *Torment*. His novels have been translated into thirteen languages. He lives in New Hampshire with his wife and three children.

Visit him online at: www.jeremyrobinsononline.com.

Sean Ellis is the international bestselling author of *Magic Mirror* and several other novels. He is a frequent collaborator with Jeremy Robinson, responsible for *Prime, Callsign: King – The Brainstorm Trilogy, Savage* and *Cannibal.* He is a veteran of Operation Enduring Freedom, and has a Bachelor of Science degree in Natural Resources Policy from Oregon State University. He lives in Arizona, where he divides his time between writing, adventure sports and trying to figure out how to save the world.

Visit him online at: seanellisthrillers.webs.com.

David Wood is the international bestselling author The Dane Maddock Adventures, the popular action-adventure series, as well as several standalone works and two series for young adults. He collaborated with Jeremy Robinson on *Callsign: Queen*. Under his David Debord pen name, he is the author of the *Absent Gods* fantasy series. When not writing, he co-hosts the AuthorCast podcast (formerly ThrillerCast). David and his family live in Santa Fe, New Mexico.

Visit him online at: www.davidwoodweb.com.

Edward G. Talbot is the pen name for two authors. Ed Parrot lives in Massachusetts and has long been fascinated with turning ideas into written words. Jason Derrig lives in Maine and likes to tell stories, especially about conspiracies. The two authors have collaborated to create a brand of thriller that keeps the stakes high, while not taking itself too seriously. They co-authored *Callsign: Rook* with Jeremy Robinson.

Visit them online at: www.edwardgtalbot.com.

David McAfee is the international bestselling author of *33 A.D.* and several other books, including the award-winning sequel, *61 A.D.*, both of which have recently been optioned for film by Winkler Films in Hollywood. David co-authored *Callsign: Bishop* with Jeremy Robinson. He lives in Tennessee with his wife and children, and is currently putting the finishing touches on the third book in his *Bachiyr* series, *79 A.D.*

Visit him online at: www.McAfeeland.wordpress.com.

Ethan Cross is the pen name of the international bestselling author of *The Shepherd*. He lives and writes in Illinois with his wife, three kids, and two Shih Tzus. His dream of telling stories on a grand scale came to fruition with the release of his first book, which went on to become an international bestseller published in several countries and languages. Ethan followed this up with more great titles like *The Prophet*, *The Cage* and *Blind Justice*. He co-authored *Callsign: Knight* with Jeremy Robinson. His latest book is the third installment of the Shepherd series, *Father of Fear*, released in 2014.

Visit him online at: www.ethancross.com.

Kane Gilmour is the international bestselling author of *The Crypt of Dracula*. He co-authored *Ragnarok* and *Omega*, the fourth and fifth novels in the Jack Sigler/Chess Team series. He also writes his own thriller novels, including the popular Jason Quinn novel, *Resurrect*. In addition to his work in novels, Kane works with artist Scott P. Vaughn on the sci-fi noir webcomic, *Warbirds of Mars*. He lives with his family in Vermont.

Visit him online at: kanegilmour.com.

J. Kent Holloway is the international bestselling author of *The Curse of One-Eyed Jack* and other edge-of-your-seat paranormal thrillers and mysteries. A real-life paranormal investigator and 'Legend Tripper,' he explores the realms of myth, folklore and the unknown, in the southeast United States in his spare time. When not writing or scouring the globe for ghosts, cryptids and all manner of legends, he works as a forensic death investigator. Kent co-authors the Jack Sigler Continuum series with Jeremy Robinson.

Visit him online at: kenthollowayonline.com.

ABOUT THE ILLUSTRATOR

Christian Guldager is a Danish illustrator living in the cold north of Scandinavia with his wife, son and a whole lot of Indiana Jones collectibles. He draws and paints whenever he can get away with it. In addition, he also writes the young adult series *Skyworld*, available in Danish and English.

Visit www.chrisguldager.com to see more of his work.

ALSO BY JEREMY ROBINSON

Standalone Novels

The Didymus Contingency

Raising The Past

Beneath

Antarktos Rising

Kronos

Uprising (aka: *Xom-B*)

Flood Rising

MirrorWorld (2015)

Kaiju Novels

Island 731

Project Nemesis

Project Maigo

Project 731

SecondWorld Novels

SecondWorld

Nazi Hunter: Atlantis

(aka: *I Am Cowboy*)

The Antarktos Saga

The Last Hunter – Descent

The Last Hunter – Pursuit

The Last Hunter – Ascent

The Last Hunter – Lament

The Last Hunter – Onslaught

The Last Hunter – Collected Edition

The Jack Sigler Novels

Prime

Pulse

Instinct

Threshold

Ragnarok

Omega

Savage

Cannibal

Jack Sigler Continuum Novellas

Guardian

Patriot (2015)

Cerberus Group Novels

Herculean (2015)

The Chesspocalypse Novellas

Callsign: King

Callsign: Queen

Callsign: Rook

Callsign: King – Underworld

Callsign: Bishop

Callsign: Knight

Callsign: Deep Blue

Callsign: King – Blackout

ALSO BY JEREMY ROBINSON

Chess Team Novella
Collected Editions
The Brainstorm Trilogy
Callsign – Tripleshot
Callsign – Doubleshot

Chess Team Universe Guide
Endgame

Horror Novels
(Written as Jeremy Bishop)
Torment
The Sentinel
The Raven
Refuge

ALSO BY SEAN ELLIS

Jack Sigler / Chess Team Series
Callsign: King
Callsign: King – Underworld
Callsign: King – Blackout
Prime
Savage
Cannibal

Cerberus Group Novels
Herculean (2015)

The Nick Kismet Adventures
The Shroud of Heaven
Into the Black
The Devil You Know
Fortune Favors

The Adventures of Dodge Dalton
In the Shadow of Falcon's Wings
At the Outpost of Fate
On the High Road to Oblivion

Dark Trinity: The Mira Raiden Adventures
Ascendant
Descendant

Jade Ihara Adventures
Oracle
(with David Wood)

Standalone Novels
Magic Mirror
The Sorcerer's Ghost
Flood Rising
(with Jeremy Robinson)

Secret Agent X
The Sea Wraiths
Masterpiece of Vengeance
The Scar

David Wood's Dane and Bones Origins Series
Hell Ship

Steven Savile's Ogmios Team
Wargod

Edited Anthology
The Game

ALSO BY DAVID WOOD

Chesspocalypse Novellas
Callsign: Queen

The Dane Maddock Adventures
Dourado
Cibola
Quest
Icefall
Buccaneer
Atlantis

Jade Ihara Adventures
Oracle
(with Sean Ellis)

Dane and Bones Origins
Freedom
(with Sean Sweeney)
Hell Ship
(with Sean Ellis)
Liberty
(with Edward G. Talbot)
Dead Ice
(with Steven Savile)
Splashdown
(with Rick Chesler)

Standalone Works
Into the Woods
(with David S. Wood)
Dark Rite
(with Alan Baxter)
The Zombie-Driven Life

The Dunn Kelly Mysteries
You Suck
Bite Me
(Forthcoming)

Writing as David Debord
The Silver Serpent
Keeper of the Mists
The Gates of Iron
(forthcoming)
The Impostor Prince
(with Ryan A. Span -
forthcoming)

ALSO BY EDWARD G. TALBOT

Chesspocalypse Novellas
Callsign: Rook

Novels
New World Orders
2012: The Fifth World
Liberty
(with David Wood)

**Half Novels
(Terrorist Chronicles
Thrillers)**
Alive From New York
Alive From America

ALSO BY DAVID McAFEE

Collaborations with Jeremy Robinson
Callsign: Bishop
Refuge Book 4: Ashes and Dust

Bachiyr Series
33 A.D.
61 A.D.
After – Taras and Theron: Beyond Jerusalem

Standalone novels
Saying Goodbye to the Sun
Nasty Little F!#*ers
Old Sins

Collections
The Lake and 17 Other Stories
Devil Music and 18 Other Stories

Novellas
The Dead Woman
(The Dead Man Series #4)
Dante's Disciple
(with Marty McKay)

Nonfiction
Livin' La Vida Papa

ALSO BY ETHAN CROSS

Chesspocalypse Novellas
Callsign: Knight

Shepherd Series
The Shepherd
The Prophet
Father of Fear

Standalone Novels
Blind Justice

Novellas
The Cage

ALSO BY KANE GILMOUR

Collaborations with Jeremy Robinson

Callsign: Deep Blue
Ragnarok
Omega
Refuge: Book 5 - Bonfires Burning
Bright
Endgame

The Jason Quinn Series

Resurrect
Frozen (2015)

Nostalgic Horror Novellas

The Crypt of Dracula
The Monster of Frankenstein
(2015)

Edited Anthology

Warbirds of Mars: Stories of the Fight!
(with Scott P. Vaughn)

Webcomic

Warbirds of Mars

ALSO BY J. KENT HOLLOWAY

Jack Sigler Continuum Series
Guardian
Patriot (2015)

The ENIGMA Directive Series
Primal Thirst
Sirens' Song
Devil's Child

The Dark Hollows Mystery Series
The Curse of One-Eyed Jack
The Dirge of Briarsnare Marsh

The Knightshade Legacy Series
The Djinn

The Legend of the Winterking
The Crown of Nandur

Short Stories
"Freakshow" (An ENIGMA Directive Short Story)
"Masquerade at One Thousand Feet"
"Haunted Melody" (A Meikle Bay Horror Short Story)

"JEREMY ROBINSON IS THE NEXT JAMES ROLLINS."
— CHRIS KUZNESKI, NY TIMES BESTSELLING AUTHOR

HERCULEAN

A CERBERUS GROUP NOVEL

JEREMY ROBINSON

AND SEAN ELLIS

INTERNATIONAL BESTSELLING DUO OF SAVAGE AND CANNIBAL

Coming in 2015

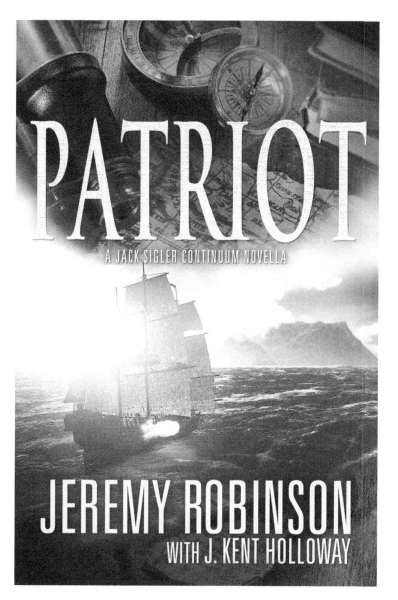

PATRIOT

A JACK SIGLER CONTINUUM NOVELLA

JEREMY ROBINSON

WITH J. KENT HOLLOWAY

Coming in 2015

Made in the USA
Monee, IL
31 March 2022